Praise for *STRESSED in the U.S.*

"Meg Van Deusen offers a fascinating glimpse into the alarming epidemic of stress in the US. Filled with compelling stories, practical solutions and a wealth of empirical evidence, this book is sure to be a 'go-to' solution for anyone wanting to live with less stress and more mindfulness."

—Sean Fargo, former Buddhist monk and founder of
Mindfulness Exercises

"Dr. Van Deusen's book provides a holistic and compelling overview of the stresses and challenges we all face and the ramifications for our relationships, communities and systems of care. This book will surely add to the literature on stress and provide readers with a fresh look at how to live healthier lives."

—Mona Delahooke, PhD, psychologist, and author of *Beyond Behaviors: Using
Brain Science and Compassion to Understand and Solve Children's Behavioral Challenges*

"In this wise and illuminating book, Meg Van Deusen reveals the developmental roots of our current epidemic of chronic stress, the silent killer that threatens our health and well-being. Drawing insights from her own life and work as well as the latest research, she offers powerful practices that can heal and transform our lives. An important book for these challenging times."

—Diane Dreher, author of *The Tao of Inner Peace and Your Personal Renaissance*

"This is the perfect book to help you realize why you (or someone you love) is stressed, how that stress is making a physiological and emotional impact, and what might help bring relief. Research driven, yet practical enough to be useful right away, Dr. Van Deusen's thorough coverage of attachment theory, technology use, and mindfulness is peppered with tips and tools for reversing the tsunami of stress inherent in our everyday lives. This is a book that you'll read and share and everyone will be better for it."

—Doreen Dodgen-Magee, author of *Deviced! Balancing Life and Technology in a
Digital World*

"In this compelling book, Meg Van Deusen delivers on her promise of sharing effective navigational tools to help us make our way safely across the troubled waters of our times."

—Dr. Vincent Atchity, President and CEO, Mental Health Colorado

STRESSED

in the

U.S.

12 Tools to Tackle Anxiety, Loneliness, Tech Addiction, and More

MEG VAN DEUSEN, PhD

STORY MERCHANT BOOKS · LOS ANGELES · 2019

Stressed in the U.S.

ISBN-13: 978-1-7340324-1-3

Story Merchant Books
400 S. Burnside Avenue, #11B
Los Angeles, CA 90036
www.storymerchantbooks.com

www.529bookdesign.com
Cover: Claire Moore
Interior: Lauren Michelle

For all of you who are suffering from any form of stress,
we need each other to navigate this life.
I hope this book helps you navigate yours with greater ease.

ACKNOWLEDGMENTS

I wrote this book during what was the most stressful year and a half of my life. Just when I began to recover from one shock, another would hit. I wondered if the universe was testing the solidity of my work. Am I being challenged to implement the twelve tools with unwavering presence? One thing I know is that if I hadn't had the love and support of my loyal husband, Eric, the belief in me of my wise children, Keenan and Julian, both of whom have the ability to be candid without being critical, and the encouragement of my now ninety-seven-year-old mother, Doris Orsi, I probably wouldn't have been able to write it. All of you are beautiful souls who have graced my life in ways that are too many to count. Thank you.

To Ken Atchity, my literary manager, although you may not have realized it, you appeared to me like an anchor in a storm and for that I will be forever grateful. You took a chance on me, believed in me and gave me a portal to the world of authorship. You are sharp, wise, and compassionate—a golden combination for which I am truly appreciative. Thank you.

To my editor, Lisa Cerasoli, whose humor, vivacity, and candor was like an array of twinkling stars amidst a sometimes-murky sky. I can't imagine working with anyone more enthusiastic and real. Thank you for the phone calls, video chats, emails, and text exchanges that have helped shaped this book into the living thing it is today!

To Claire Moore and Lauren Michelle, both from 529 Books, thank you for your cover and interior design work, respectively. What a pleasure it was to work with both of you!

To everyone at Story Merchant Books, thank you for your expert editing and publishing advice and navigation throughout this process.

To my writing teacher, Jim Degnan, from Santa Clara University, your words and encouragement still echo in my brain some thirty-five years later. I wouldn't have ventured to write this book had you not instilled your confidence in me when I was a young undergraduate.

Thank you to Diane Dreher and Victoria Bennion. Your support and enthusiasm, not to mention expert advice, boosted me to the next level.

Thank you to those who took the time to talk and share their expertise with me: David Wallin, Thomas Plante, Mona Delahooke, Teiahsha Bankhead, Theodore Grover, Jason Ong, William De Paulo, Hans Jangaard, and Rogene Eichler West. And thank you to those I interviewed who wish to remain anonymous. Your openness and willingness to tell your personal stories have enhanced the meaning of this book.

Thank you to my dear friends, colleagues, and readers of my work: Aida Salas, Marianne Teleki, Nathan Hunter, Donna Duhe, Sean Fargo, Abby Brown, and Glenn Maarse. Your input was authentic and invaluable. I so appreciate the time you took amidst your busy schedules to read my passages, listen to my woes and provide me with honest feedback. You are my tribe.

Thank you to my dear friend, Gabriele Hanauer-Mader, who died unexpectedly during the writing of this work. You were an excellent journalist, trailblazer, mother, sister, daughter and friend. I will always cherish your friendship and support of my writing.

To my sister, Janet, who has taken time away from her work to help our aging mother so I could complete mine. My love for you is decades long and deep.

To my late father, Charles Van Deusen, although I only had you for twenty years, you taught me to appreciate the beauty of the English language, the art of writing, and so much more…thank you.

And, last, but never least, thank you to all my clients, both past and present, who courageously entered therapy, entrusted me with your hearts, minds, and souls and bravely made yourselves vulnerable enough to change. You are the biggest inspiration for this book.

CONTENTS

STRESSED *in the* U.S.

12 Tools to Tackle Anxiety, Loneliness, Tech Addiction, and More

MEG VAN DEUSEN, PhD

"*Because American culture as a whole tends to favor and recognize the yearning for agency and independence to the exclusion of the yearning for inclusion and connection, we can sometimes fail to recognize this latter yearning in ourselves.*"

—Robert Kegan

INTRODUCTION

In September of 2001, I was on a tango cruise in Alaska with my husband, Eric, when a Swedish man from our dance class met us in the hallway. "Did you hear the news? A plane hit the Twin Towers in New York. They think it was an attack."

"What?" I asked.

"I'm so sorry for your country," he said and walked away, shaking his head.

Eric and I arrived at class where everyone was discussing what would come to be known as 9/11, uttering phrases such as "Osama Bin Laden...terrorist act...hundreds dead...maybe more...." After intermittently talking about the news, many of us headed back to our cabins to watch it live. The video of the United Airlines 767 plowing into the Twin Towers was horrifying. Watching the footage, Eric and I woke up to the fact that our country was under a terrorist attack and we were twenty-five hundred miles away from our son, whom we'd left with godparents and grandparents in Seattle. To be so far away from our only child during what was later determined to be the worst terrorist attack in US history was anxiety-provoking.

The ensuing hours consisted of numerous phone calls back home. We first touched base with our son via the ship's phone as the cruise line was allowing passengers to make as many calls as they needed. We then called our friend, Marcus, who routinely piloted the Boston and DC routes on United Airlines and were relieved to find he was not on duty that day. Then we contacted relatives and friends in San Francisco, Los Angeles, and especially New York to be sure they were alive and safe. The general impulse was to connect with loved ones, as our sense of safety had been greatly compromised.

Despite the unpredictable and destabilizing circumstances of 9/11, we couldn't have been in a better place—on a ship among the Alaskan glaciers. Boats were not grounded like airplanes, so our trip continued sailing from one port to the next, more isolated than most from the mainland news, which seemed to assist in reducing our anxiety. Our tango friends, from all regions in the United States and many countries around the world, offered comfort. One woman was terrified and then relieved to hear that her daughter, who had been on her way to her first day of work in the Twin Towers, hadn't yet arrived when the first plane hit. Another couple spoke of the constant stress they endured growing up in South Africa during apartheid when bombings were a frequent occurrence. As a group, we talked, cried, and supported one another. This community, albeit a very new one, helped us digest an unimaginable tragedy. I believe that it was this sense of immediate support, and what psychoanalyst D.W. Winnicott refers to as a "holding environment," that allowed me to sleep those initial days, despite the fact that our world, as we knew it, had changed forever.

9/11 marked a national shift in what psychoanalyst John Bowlby called "secure attachment." To have a secure attachment to your parent means you feel safe and free to explore the environment without fear of abandonment, engulfment, or abuse. As humans, we also have secure and insecure attachments to groups we belong to outside our nuclear family, including an attachment to our nation.[1] Americans had enjoyed a terrorist-free environment for decades. Even the Pearl Harbor attack, although devastating, wasn't as intimate and unprovoked as 9/11. We generally felt safe in our country. Most of us didn't feel threatened by international terrorism on our own soil.

After 9/11, my secure attachment to the United States became insecure. The reality that we were no longer immune to terrorism sunk in once we returned home from the cruise, as subsequent stories of the thousands of lives lost under such brutal circumstances appeared nonstop over all forms of media. It was then that my sleep patterns, which had been disrupted since the birth of my child, got worse. After 9/11, I didn't leave my kids (I had a second child in 2004) for more than a day for many years. I was no longer the same person, nor were my feelings about national security the same.

As if the 9/11 terrorist attacks weren't enough to shake us, in 2006, Al Gore came out with his acclaimed book, *An Inconvenient Truth: The Crisis of Global Warming*,[2] which outlined in stark detail how global warming has put our very existence as a human race in grave danger. Dystopian literature abounded, especially in teen novels. Anxiety among patients in my practice grew. In that same year, my son chose to do his first-ever science project on the cause of global warming. He was six years old. Until global warming became a household term, many people hadn't thought much about the planet dying. Most of us had gone through life assuming it would be here forever—that *we* would be here forever. Indeed, research is now demonstrating that even the *concept* of climate change can affect our emotional well-being[3] and further disrupt the secure attachment we once had with the place we Americans call home.

Then, in 2008, a mere seven years after 9/11, the recession proved to be the biggest economic hit to our country since the Great Depression. By this time, I had an eight-year-old and a four-year-old, and my husband and I were in business for ourselves, making our financial security feel about as stable as marshmallow floating on a river. The middle class was shrinking, and my husband and I felt squeezed into a debt we could not have predicted and surely hadn't planned for. Saving for college or retirement became impossible. Whether it was rising unemployment (the rate was at 7 percent and eventually reached 10 percent in 2009[4]), war (the US was involved in two at the time), climate change, or the increased awareness of mass shootings, it seemed like everywhere we turned, something threatened our well-being. Would we be working into our eighties just to keep afloat? Would climate change limit our access to natural resources? And, worse than either of those worries was the fear that one of our children could be shot at school one day, just as the innocent students of Columbine or Virginia Tech had been. (Sandy Hook, Parkland, and myriad other school shootings had not yet occurred.)

Abraham Maslow's hierarchy of needs demonstrates how having basic needs met creates various levels of security and, therefore, the ability to grow psychologically. So, if my husband and I, as white, middle-class Americans who had each other to lean on were stressed, how was the oppressed, single, African American mother feeling? A 2015 survey conducted by the American Psychological Association reported that 78 percent of blacks in the United States were stressed because of money issues.[5] In addition, Latinos were the most stressed of all Americans, and the two other ethnic minorities studied (Native Americans and Asians) reported higher stress levels than whites. While money was reported as the biggest stressor among all groups, work (or lack thereof) came in as a close second. Money and work were becoming harder to obtain during the recession, and while my husband and I were hit, minority groups were trampled by the challenge of it.

Finally, in 2016, one of the most historic elections in US history took place. Amidst questions about Hillary Clinton's emails, rumors of Russian interference in our election, and outrage over Donald Trump's *Access Hollywood* tape, in which he bragged about sexually violating women, Americans were seemingly divided and in an uproar. Then, when Trump was surprisingly elected, a downward spiral of our American values began to occur, and people, especially minorities (who made up 38.4 percent of the US population in 2015 and are expected to exceed 50 percent by 2020), were scared for their safety and security. Their fear was in response to the president's attempt to ban and deport certain ethnic groups, remove transgender people from the military, and push for a healthcare bill that would have taken millions of Americans off their health insurance, resulting in catastrophic numbers of health problems and even death among our residents. Protests abounded, and stress in the US reached an all-time high.[6]

Amid the fallout of 9/11, the daunting reality of climate change, and the economic impact of the Great Recession, were Mark Zuckerberg and Steve Jobs. Zuckerberg had launched Facebook in 2004, uniting long-lost friends and giving people the opportunity to air their daily thoughts online. Facebook also consumed enormous amounts of time for Americans, keeping them glued to their screens as they searched for "friends." By 2016, Zuckerberg stated that Americans spent an average of fifty minutes a day on Facebook, which was approximately forty-six minutes more a day than most teens spent reading.[7] As if that weren't invasive enough for the American people, in 2018, Facebook admitted that a security breach had compromised the personal information of millions of Americans, creating massive mistrust in the company. There is no doubt that social media has made us more vulnerable, and vulnerability without trust is stressful.

Just three years after Facebook hit the scene, Jobs created the greatest device humans had seen since the television—the iPhone! It could make calls, type instant messages, take photos, record your voice, and, yes, access Facebook. Everyone had to have one. And thus, came the dawning of the age of the bent-necked cell phone addict who knows more about a stranger doing ollies on his skateboard (because it happens to be trending on YouTube) than they do about their next-door neighbor.

The iPhone (and the Android, too) have kept us well connected. Sort of. We can contact many more people in a day than we used to; we just don't talk to them. We can supposedly get much more done with email and text messaging because both forms of communication are now a fingertip away—and productivity is an American value. But, can we relax without pills or booze or endless mindfulness meditations? In her book, *Alone Together: Why We Expect More from Technology and Less from Each Other*, Sherry Turkle calls this attachment to our devices "the cyborg life."[8]

How is "the cyborg life" relevant to our stress levels? Well, we are in an era of information overload. Because of the accessibility of news, and because we are easily reached through many forms of messaging, including unwanted robocalls, we are constantly "on." This creates a chronic feeling of overwhelm and difficulty knowing where the boundaries lie between work and rest. If we never get to truly "turn off," if we're always being pinged for one reason or another, we don't get the rejuvenation our bodies and minds need in order to handle stress in the first place.

In addition, psychiatrist John Bowlby's psychological theory of attachment, along with psychologist Allan Schore's groundbreaking work in interpersonal neurobiology, illustrates how we have lost visual and auditory attunement to one another—an attunement that is not only necessary for brain development, but for managing stress. Bowlby's theory postulated that a child's emotional security was heavily influenced by whether his caregivers gave him emotionally attuned responses as a child, most of which include eye contact. Eye contact and facial mirroring is key to developing a secure attachment to one's caregiver. Furthermore, a child's attachment experience informs his or her adult experience of close relationships, something humans need for well-being. And secure, close relationships inform our resilience. Allan Shore, PhD, a psychologist at the University of California, Los Angeles states, "Resilience in the face of stress is an ultimate indicator of attachment capacity."[9] If parents are on their phones instead of interacting with their babies, how might this be affecting our little ones' brains, especially if they, too, sit in the stroller with a digital screen?

Not only is secure attachment necessary for resilience, sleep also seems to be dependent upon it. Sleep has become an American obsession. Go to the grocery store and peruse the magazine aisle. There will likely be an article on sleep in one of the current issues of *Good Housekeeping, Time,* or *Popular Science,* to name a few. Why all the buzz? Insomnia is a growing problem for people who are adamantly trying to do everything right so they can induce healthy sleep but are unable to achieve their aim. In addition, societal pressure to get more done drives people to believe that six hours of sleep a night is all they can afford in their busy, American lives.

More than this, the epidemic of American obesity places another burden on sleep. Obesity, which is often connected to stress, can cause sleep apnea, a condition in which one's air passages are constricted, causing frequent waking at night. The result is that sleepers with this condition do not get restorative sleep and, therefore, are at risk for an array of other medical problems.

Then, there is addiction to electronic devices—something that researchers are finding can interrupt sleep even when people have put down their phones and tablets and turned out the lights. These astounding and widespread circumstances are compromising Americans in ways that are too numerous to count. While the fields of psychology and medicine try to do something about it (the US has more than 2,500 sleep clinics today), why is it not enough? I will look at the debate about whether we aren't getting enough sleep or are simply not getting restorative sleep and theorize about how this is connected to an insecure attachment and, therefore, increased stress.

In this book, I take a sober look at how the aforementioned changes to our American lives have created unrest, anxiety, loneliness, and even gut imbalance, culminating in a stressed-out society. In psychology, if we know what causes a condition, we have a better chance of curing it. It's imperative, as psychologists and as lay citizens, that we pause and look at some of the underlying circumstances for stress, so we can understand how to address stress. If we want to give up the Xanax or Ambien, it's crucial we admit our lack of connectedness to one another, despite living in the illusion that we're more connected than ever.

By reviewing the research and examining the trends and stories in my private practice, I explore how rising stress is affecting our nervous systems and our relationships. In Chapter One, I define stress to give the reader an understanding of what it really is, including the difference between good stress and bad stress. I then illuminate the current stressors that plague us most as Americans and suggest how they are intertwined.

In Chapter Two, I explain attachment theory and talk about why it is relevant to current stress in the US. I discuss how our current American culture is threatening a secure attachment to ourselves, each other, and our nation. If our sense of security is shaken, we lose our resilience to stress. I discuss what we might do about that.

In Chapter Three, I bust the myths of mindfulness and explain why it is a necessary solution to our current stress levels, even though many people don't feel they have time for it.

In Chapter Four, I address the increasing rate of anxiety in our country, explaining how anxiety, stress, and insecure attachment are related. I break anxiety into three categories: generalized anxiety (which has to do with our current, everyday worries), social anxiety (which centers on fear of others' judgment), and death anxiety (which is subconsciously related to the fear we'll lose our lives to terrorism, climate change, or domestic gun violence, all of which are on Americans' minds). Each section will offer healthy responses to the type of anxiety presented.

In Chapter Five, I look at why so many Americans suffer from loneliness, even though we've added twenty-three million people to our US population in the last ten years. Because loneliness is a stressor, I take a particular look at the sturdiness of our attachments to one another and discuss how to strengthen them.

In Chapter Six, I delve into the rapidly growing field of technology and how we may not have adequately prepared ourselves for some of its pitfalls, how it may be compounding our stress, and how we can benefit from it when using it for the better good. Everything from smartphones to artificially intelligent robots will be explored.

In Chapter Seven, I illuminate the pervasive problem of information overload (that is, grappling with robocalls, emails, text messages, media exposure, and more). There are ways to intervene on this, decreasing the stressful feeling of chronic bombardment.

In Chapter Eight, I look closely at the phenomenon of sleep loss or poor sleep quality (which is it, really?) and how attachment theory, along with breakthroughs in neuroscience, may hold the answer. After all, the better we sleep, the less we are prone to stress.

In Chapter Nine, I tackle the impact of stress on our bodies, looking at everything from opioid addiction to the gut microbiome to telomeres. There has been great interest recently in what makes for a healthy gut, as it is deemed the hard drive of our immune systems—this means it takes a big hit when we are stressed. And telomeres (the little caps on the ends of our chromosomes), well, stress seems to predict their health and, therefore, our longevity.

In Chapter Ten, I provide hope for a better future. I summarize the solutions to the problems that were introduced in the previous chapters. I break them down into twelve tools readers can implement to decrease stress, increase secure attachment, and enhance well-being in the United States.

As you read, determine what resonates with you and what you may have in common with your neighbor. With the ideas brought forth in this book, perhaps we can, together, begin to ease our worries, calm our nerves, and nurture our bonds with one another—making a dent in stress in the US.

STRESSED *in the* U.S.

1

WHAT IS STRESS?

"Everyone knows what stress is, but nobody really knows."

—Hans Selye

stress *(noun):* 1. the non-specific response of the body to any demand for change. 2. a state of mental or emotional strain or tension resulting from adverse or very demanding circumstances.

I'm running as fast as I can and I'm having trouble breathing. My heart flutters and seems to skip a beat. I wonder if I'm going to pass out or, worse, have a heart attack. I'm aware that my hands are sweating. I call after my older sister, who is some twenty steps ahead.

"I can't run anymore!"

She turns her head just enough to glance back. "Come on!"

This was me at seven years old after my sister, the neighbor kid, and I threw acorns at a passing car and hit the driver—who turned out to be an off-duty policeman. He stopped his car and started chasing us. I honestly thought I was going to have a heart attack as I sprinted up a path of stairs, trying to catch up to my sister and neighbor. I'd never before felt my heart beat so forcefully and rapidly. I was terrified of being caught and having something bad happen to me. My physiological and psychological responses were that of *acute stress.*

Many of us experience acute stress at various points in our lives. Barbara Streisand reported to Oprah in 2009 that she didn't perform for twenty-seven years because of stage fright. Stage fright is a stress response to the fear of losing control from making a mistake. Oprah asked Barbara about the stage fright:

"Where did that come from?'

"Well, when I was in front of 135,000 people in Central Park— my free concert in Central Park—I forgot the words [to the song] and it sort of triggered this feeling that I would forget the words. I didn't perform again until they discovered teleprompters."[10]

Barbara's embarrassing moment of forgetting the words (losing control of her performance) lodged itself into her mind and caused her stress when she thought about going on stage again.

Most of us have talked about being "stressed out" at some point in our lives. Sometimes, we feel stress when we feel in danger or feel helpless, like how I felt when I was running from the policeman. We also experience stress when something threatens our physical or emotional well-being, like Barbara's fear of embarrassing herself. Usually, people know they are stressed because they feel it physically. Our muscles tighten, our heart rate increases, we sweat, our breathing becomes more rapid, and we often can't think clearly.

Despite these jarring symptoms, not all stress is bad. We need some degree of stress in order to stay alive. If our ancestors hadn't flinched at the sight of a cougar, they might have been eaten. If we don't jump out of the way of a speeding car, we'd likely get hit. Stress moves us toward self-preservation, like the stress that instinctively caused me to run from the scary, off-duty policeman.

On a day-to-day level, stress can motivate us to study for that exam or meet a work deadline. The origin of the word *motivate* comes from the Latin word *motus,* meaning motion. In this way, a positive effect of stress is that it gets us off the couch and moving toward a goal. In the US, we love to accomplish things, and a little stress can help us achieve that aim.

Stressors themselves can be either positive or negative. The Holmes-Rahe Life Stress Inventory created by psychiatrists Thomas Holmes and Richard Rahe in 1967 lists forty-three life stressors that were researched and correlated to physical illness. The more stressors one has, or the more intensely one experiences stress in a year's time, the more likely that person will develop an illness. On this list, however, are several life events that one could deem positive. For example, number seven is marriage, number twelve is pregnancy, and number twenty-five is an outstanding major achievement.

The Holmes-Rahe Life Stress Inventory
The Social Readjustment Rating Scale

INSTRUCTIONS: Mark down the point value of each of these life events that has happened to you during the previous year. Total these associated points.

Life Event	Mean Value
1. Death of spouse	100
2. Divorce	73
3. Marital Separation from mate	65
4. Detention in jail or other institution	63
5. Death of a close family member	63
6. Major personal injury or illness	53
7. Marriage	50
8. Being fired at work	47
9. Marital reconciliation with mate	45
10. Retirement from work	45
11. Major change in the health or behavior of a family member	44
12. Pregnancy	40
13. Sexual Difficulties	39
14. Gaining a new family member (i.e., birth, adoption, older adult moving in, etc)	39
15. Major business readjustment	39
16. Major change in financial state (i.e., a lot worse or better off than usual)	38
17. Death of a close friend	37
18. Changing to a different line of work	36
19. Major change in the number of arguments w/spouse (i.e., either a lot more or a lot less than usual regarding child rearing, personal habits, etc.)	35
20. Taking on a mortgage (for home, business, etc..)	31
21. Foreclosure on a mortgage or loan	30
22. Major change in responsibilities at work (i.e. promotion, demotion, etc.)	29
23. Son or daughter leaving home (marriage, attending college, joined mil.)	29
24. In-law troubles	29
25. Outstanding personal achievement	28
26. Spouse beginning or ceasing work outside the home	26
27. Beginning or ceasing formal schooling	26
28. Major change in living condition (new home, remodeling, deterioration of neighborhood or home etc.)	25
29. Revision of personal habits (dress manners, associations, quitting smoking)	24
30. Troubles with the boss	23
31. Major changes in working hours or conditions	20
32. Changes in residence	20
33. Changing to a new school	20
34. Major change in usual type and/or amount of recreation	19
35. Major change in church activity (i.e., a lot more or less than usual)	19
36. Major change in social activities (clubs, movies, visiting, etc.)	18
37. Taking on a loan (car, tv, freezer, etc)	17
38. Major change in sleeping habits (a lot more or a lot less than usual)	16
39. Major change in number of family get-togethers ("")	15
40. Major change in eating habits (a lot more or less food intake, or very different meal hours or surroundings)	15
41. Vacation	13
42. Major holidays	12
43. Minor violations of the law (traffic tickets, jaywalking, disturbing the peace, etc)	11

Now, add up all the points you have to find your score.

150pts or less means a relatively low amount of life change and a low susceptibility to stress-induced health breakdown.

150 to 300 pts implies about a 50% chance of a major health breakdown in the next 2 years.

300pts or more raises the odds to about 80%, according to the Holmes-Rahe statistical prediction model.

Why are these seemingly positive experiences considered stressful? Because any kind of change can make us feel less in control, and not feeling in control can be stressful. In other words, when we are familiar with something, we usually don't see it as a threat. But when something new occurs outside our comfort zone, it tends to rattle us. There is a thin line between excitement and fear. And there can be a thin line between *eustress* (positive stress) and *distress* (negative stress). Take, for example, me writing this book. While the possibility of publishing a book on stress is exciting, the thought of it sometimes makes me nervous. I'm not sure how this is all going to turn out. Will it be good enough? Will people read it? I'm not entirely in control of those things. So, when I think of them, I feel slightly queasy, even though what motivates me to write would be considered *eustress*.

While a mild and fleeting queasiness in the gut from *eustress* isn't likely to cause chronic illness, more sustained gut queasiness from *distress* could. People who are under daily *distress* are at an increased risk for developing a host of physical and psychological ailments. In fact, 77 percent of Americans say stress causes them physical symptoms, and 73 percent report psychological symptoms.[11] Some of the most common symptoms are frequent headaches and jaw pain, lightheadedness, cold and sweaty hands, trouble concentrating, forgetfulness, and insomnia. What is the physiological mechanism that creates these symptoms? Let's take a look.

When a change in our environment leaves us feeling out of control or unable to adapt to the shift, our brain activates the amygdala, which is the area responsible for emotional processing. If it determines true danger, it sends a signal to the hypothalamus, the part of the brain that activates the fight or flight response. The fight or flight response sends signals to the pituitary gland and the adrenal medulla, activating them to release the stress hormones *cortisol* and

4

epinephrine (otherwise known as *adrenaline*). In turn, these hormones prepare our bodies to run from (flee) or take on (fight) the stressor.

How do these hormones do this? They release glucose from the liver and fat molecules into the bloodstream for more energy. They increase our heart rate, so we have more blood flow to our muscles in order to flee or fight. They dilate our lungs, so we take in more oxygen. They open our sweat glands to cool an overheated body. And, they dilate our pupils, so we can see better, especially in the dark. *Endorphins* get released, which allow us to fight without being deterred by pain.

There is yet another response to stress, and, while it's less common, it's no less impactful. It is the phenomenon of *freezing*. When my sister was in her early twenties, she and a family friend lived at home with my parents. They walked out the door to go to work one morning, and, in less than a minute, my mom yelled for them to come back. They rushed into the kitchen to see my father lying unconscious on the floor. He had had a heart attack. As our friend was a registered nurse, he started doing CPR. Simultaneously, he ordered my sister to move the kitchen table, so he had more room to work.

"I froze and went into a kind of stupor," my sister recalled. "I couldn't move myself, let alone the table."

Stephen Porges, PhD, a university scientist and researcher, calls what my sister experienced "the defense system of the parasympathetic nervous system." Because the flight or fight symptoms originate in the sympathetic nervous system, it is known as the main defense system against stress, while the parasympathetic nervous system is traditionally known as the calming system. However, in Dr. Porges's polyvagal theory, he describes a defense system in the parasympathetic nervous system that causes our bodies to shut down, sometimes even to the point of passing out. He attributes this process to a reptilian branch of the vagus nerve that runs from our visceral organs to the brain. Dr. Porges maintains that when we experience trauma (however mild or severe), sometimes this system gets activated and our bodies perform shutdown strategies to disappear, like when a lizard freezes to appear dead when being threatened. In addition to freezing, we may involuntarily urinate or defecate. Our oxygen supply to the brain gets cut, causing us to faint (and, in rare cases, die). It's as if our body tries to make us invisible to the threat.[12]

All of these physiological stress responses are useful for fending off an attacker, fleeing from a fire, or playing dead with a grizzly. But, imagine that your body is in a constant state of stress, and the release of these hormones are chronically occurring. Eventually, the adrenal glands will tire from relentless hard work, creating what some call *adrenal fatigue,* which makes us less able to fight or flee when an acute stressor comes along. The continued suppression of the immune system, via cortisol production, becomes the body's sustained state and we get sick more easily. In addition, the high *cortisol* levels impair the brain, causing cognitive issues (like difficulty remembering things). An increased heart rate can damage blood vessels, creating high blood pressure and heart disease. Free radicals caused by the neurotransmitter *glutamate* also lower immune response. All of these factors set us up nicely for disease.

My father died that morning on the kitchen floor. As a slim, outwardly calm person who ate a good diet, he was not a typical heart attack candidate. Could stress have caused it? After all, heart disease is the number one stress-related disease among Americans. My father had a demanding job as a corporate lawyer in San Francisco. He also tended to keep worries to himself. We'll never really know if my father suffered from undiagnosed stress, but it is something to think about for yourself. In the field of psychology, stress is sometimes referred to as the silent killer.

The policeman never did catch my sister, the neighbor, or me. My acute stress subsided when we realized we had outrun him and that we were no longer in crisis. But, once we arrived home and learned from our parents that the policeman had reported us to a neighbor, who had reported us to our parents, stress set in again. I worried my parents would be mad at me for a long time, or that they might even call the policeman to admit our fault. As a child, I hadn't yet built much resilience to stress. Other than serious discussion, I don't remember if there was an additional repercussion of our actions, as my acute stress had overshadowed any subsequent uneasiness. Its intensity stayed in my memory bank because it was the stronger experience.

In recent years, as Americans, we have become increasingly vulnerable to stress, and, it seems, less resilient in the face of it. We also seem to be more chronically stressed and, therefore, can be less aware of stress's silent yet adverse effects on our overall well-being. In order to understand why we are more vulnerable and less resistant, we must first look at the unique factors that contribute to our rising stress levels as Americans today.

The Year 2000 Marks the Spot

"The world has not warmed up very much since the millennium."

—James Lovelock

I was out to dinner some years ago with Eric, our children, and our good friend, Glenn, when we somehow got on the topic of 1970s TV shows. The adults in the group happily reminisced, and, yes, even sang *Brady Bunch* lyrics to my then-twelve- and -sixteen-year-old kids, who were undoubtedly embarrassed. They rolled their eyes.

"But those shows were so great, so simple," Glenn said.

"And so innocent," I added, thinking of how odd it was, even then, that I was using that word.

7

Just a year prior, my then-eleven-year-old had been fascinated with *Naked and Afraid*, a primetime reality TV show that details the experiences of people who willingly go into the jungle without clothes or food and are forced to find a way to survive. They wander through rough terrain with banana leaves covering their genitals, while intermittently swearing (which is "bleeped" out) in response to the predicament.

In contrast, the 1970s presented kids with *The Waltons* or *The Jeffersons* where people were not only clothed, but they lovingly said goodnight to their siblings or made us laugh with their humorous navigation of everyday struggles. Even *Taxi*, which was slightly edgier, and the crime thriller *Columbo* were tame compared to subsequent shows like the satirical *Family Guy* or *NCIS,* a show known for flashing dead bodies. It was not lost on Eric, Glenn, and me that our children's generation was more exposed to cynical and violent TV than our generation had experienced.

Yes, the Vietnam War and violent racial discrimination were simultaneously occurring in the sixties and seventies, but the vocal resistance to it sent a message of "love, not war" and, as my colleague, Delia Gerhard, has always said, "The sixties and seventies were a time of opportunity and optimism." There was a "live and let live" attitude that connoted freedom from oppression and judgment.

As we moved into the 1980s and 1990s, we still had white perspective media marketing to kids. But, *Doogie Howser, The Wonder Years,* and *The Fresh Prince of Bel-Air* didn't have to bleep out swear words. They were entertaining and made us laugh. During this time, I lived in Los Angeles, where television is a huge part of the city's culture. When the Iraq War broke out under the leadership of George Bush, my friends and I met at a bar one night where some TV actors would often gather after shooting. While we talked and even debated some of the political decision making that was occurring during the time, I remember distinctly feeling safe and secure that "this, too, shall pass," believing that the United States was, in the grand scheme of things, still the safest and most economically secure country on the planet, despite its engagement in violent conflict overseas. After all, the stars of some of these optimistic shows were two tables over, laughing and carrying on. Was TV serving to delude us or bring us relief from stress?

I am aware that I may have been protected by my race, sexual orientation, and my educated, upper-middle-class upbringing, enjoying privileges that many Americans did not. As a result, I may have felt safe and secure because of my individual circumstances, not because my country and the world were necessarily stable. Understanding how we develop secure or insecure attachments to our nation is key to identifying your own.

Nelli Ferenczi and Tara Marshall wrote the article "Exploring Attachment to the 'Homeland' and Its Association with Heritage Culture Identification" approximately eleven and a half years after 9/11.[13] In it, they explored whether attachment theory (a psychological theory of the emotional bonds babies form to their primary caregivers and how the quality of those bonds inform the baby's sense of security) can be applied to your relationship with your nation. (I will discuss attachment theory in more detail in Chapter Two.) Ferenczi and Marshall ultimately theorized that we personify nations as attachment figures (caregivers) and relate to them as we would parental figures. The researchers found that there are three distinct attachment styles people identify with when conceptualizing their connection to their nation. The first is *secure attachment*—that is the feeling of safety and security that living in the United States gives people. This ultimately lends itself to a satisfying and flourishing life. The second is *fearful attachment,* the sense that one's country cannot be trusted to keep them safe. As a result, people experience anxiety and/or preoccupation about life in the present and future. The third is *dismissive attachment,* the dismissal that one's sense of well-being has anything at all to do with one's country.

Ferenczi and Marshall found that those who had a secure attachment to their nation had stronger identification with their heritage and a greater sense of well-being (meaning they were satisfied with their lives) compared to those who had a fearful or dismissive attachment to their nation. In addition, these same securely attached people had a subjective experience of flourishing in life compared to those who had fearful or dismissive nation attachment.

It's clear to me that this supposed secure attachment Americans had grown accustomed to, even taken for granted, became visibly shaken after 9/11. No longer could one waltz through the airport lines with a Starbucks coffee in hand and a bag slung over one's shoulder. Shoes, coats, belts, pocket change, everything but your pants and shirt had to go. Carry-ons were intermittently pulled off the surveyor belt for inspection, and passports were glanced at more than once. Friends and family members were no longer allowed to see their loved ones off at the gate, forcing children and elderly people to get special passes so they could be accompanied by their parents, sons, daughters, or others to ensure safe and timely departures. Many of my friends and clients started expressing apprehension about flying at all.

In addition, children began to experience increased anxiety about how to handle stress after 9/11, despite the fact that parents seemed oblivious to this change in them.[14] Maybe parents were too preoccupied with their own worries. After all, pharmacies reported a substantial increase in adults seeking anti-anxiety medication, and 49 percent of Americans surveyed said their sense of safety and security had been shaken after 9/11. Another 62 percent of participants of the same psychological study stated they had trouble sleeping after the attack.[15]

The Great Recession was another factor in our postmillennial experience. I remember the sinking feeling I had upon learning Washington Mutual Bank was going under. I knew this was one symptom of a cascading financial slide. While many still argue today about what really caused the recession, I think it's fair to say that it was humans getting ahead of themselves. Whether it was Wall Street greed, unregulated banks, or consumerism itself, humans weren't keeping their eyes on the ball.

Among those who were hit hard were college students seeking employment after graduation. While many talk about how the millennial generation doesn't seem to have the professional drive other generations have had, the timing of their coming into the workforce may have played a role in that. *Monitor on Psychology* reported in their September 2017 issue that the percentage of students seeking college counseling grew by 30 percent between 2009 and 2014, despite college enrollment growing by a mere 5 percent. Of these higher numbers of students seeking counseling, a reported 61 percent came to the centers complaining of anxiety.

Although we've pulled through 9/11 and the recession, it seems our attachment to our country has been injured, and repair has yet to occur. This conclusion is based on APA's 2017 survey of Americans and their stress levels. A reported 61 percent worry about job security, and 62 percent worry about money. In addition, a whopping 57 percent reported that the political climate was a significant source of stress—in particular, stress regarding terrorism rose from 51 percent to 59 percent in the last months of 2016 and into January 2017.[16]

As I write this today, not only has repair not occurred, but additional acts of international and home-grown terrorism have plagued us. In 2013, six people were killed and 280 injured in the Boston Marathon attack. In 2015, the Charleston church shooting—what was deemed a domestic terrorist attack against blacks—left nine dead and one injured. Also, in 2015, a mass shooting occurred at the Regional Center in San Bernardino, California, leaving fourteen dead and twenty-two injured. Then, a mere six months later, forty-nine were killed and fifty-three were injured at a gay nightclub in Orlando, Florida. One month after Orlando, five were killed and nine were injured in the Dallas shootings. In September of 2016, thirty-four people were injured in Al-Qaeda-motivated bombings across New York and New Jersey. In 2017, fifty-nine people were killed and 546 were injured in a devastating attack at an outdoor country music festival in Las Vegas. In 2018, eleven were left dead after a gunman entered a Jewish synagogue in Pittsburgh and gunned them down. And in 2019, the back to back massacres in El Paso, Texas, and Dayton, Ohio left thirty-one people dead and dozens wounded.

These are the attacks that resulted in the highest number of death tolls and injuries since 9/11, but do not outweigh the numerous other domestic and international terrorist attacks targeting the LGBTQ communities, black communities, TSA employees, Jews, Democrats, Republicans, and law enforcement officers. By the end of 2015, CBS News reported that 69 percent of Americans believed a terrorist attack would likely occur on US soil within the next few months. And it did.

In addition to gun violence, global warming has become a hot topic in households and schools across the nation. When Al Gore lost the 2000 presidential election and went on to write and publish *An Inconvenient Truth*, people began to pay attention to the idea that our planet seemed to be dying. The book itself reached #1 on the *New York Times* Bestseller List, and its documentary film of the same name brought the climate crisis into mainstream America.

While it appears that Gore's work spearheaded a movement that has, subsequently, made substantial changes (between 2006 and 2015, solar power increased by 6,800 percent and electric cars reached $1 million in sales globally), there is still much progress to be made. CO_2

emissions are increasing (5.5 percent between 2006 and 2017), global surface temperatures continue to increase dramatically, and sea levels are rising. Yes, the 2015 Paris Agreement was a hopeful step in the right direction, and one that empowered global citizens worldwide, but President Trump's decision to pull out of that agreement may be, in part, why 57 percent of Americans say they are stressed by our political climate, and 69 percent say they are stressed about our nation's future.[17]

How are we dealing with all this? While the answer to that question is unclear, given the increase in anxiety, anti-depressant use, screen addiction, mass shootings, and suicide, one might determine "not very well." In fact, the very coping strategies many of us use for stress, such as news and social media, are increasing, not decreasing, stress levels. But most Americans are not aware of this.

The terrorist attacks of 9/11, mass gun violence, the Great Recession, global warming, and the pervasiveness of social media are all factors affecting Americans' general well-being these days. Add the silent effect technology has had on our culture in general (which I'll address extensively in Chapter Six), and we have a plethora of new stressors that have never existed before in US history. This is, indeed, a unique time for stress in the US.

Rising Anxiety in the Twenty-First Century

"To hear the phrase 'our only hope' always makes one anxious, because it means that if the only hope doesn't work, there is nothing left."

—Lemony Snicket

When my oldest son was eleven and my youngest seven, they became enthralled with *The Andy Griffith Show* (a 1960s TV series that exuded a cozy, lighthearted feeling of small-town America). While the show took place when national angst and tragedy was particularly prevalent (in 1961, the United States narrowly escaped nuclear war with Cuba;

in 1963, President Kennedy was assassinated; in 1968, a hopeful Martin Luther King, who called out our racist culture, was shot and killed; and, as the decade closed, US involvement in the bloody Vietnam War grew), it depicted a quiet, rural life reflective of simplicity and comfort.

During one episode, in which "Aunt Bee" makes a lovely pie for Andy, my older son asked if there was such a place as Mayberry and, if so, could we live there? I had been aware that his postmillennial life had sometimes left him heavyhearted regarding the future of our planet, with the increasing threat of gun violence and worry of terrorism. The thought that a place like Mayberry existed, where people were safe, and the jail was a two-cell operation designed to temporarily house the occasional "derelict" was (despite its obvious lack of diversity) refreshing and desirable to him. The fictional town of Mayberry inspired in my son a longing for community, physical safety, and simplicity. While he may have felt secure in his family, once he stepped outside the door, the threat of another school lockdown, the eeriness of another warm winter, and the feeling of vulnerability to technological hacking and attacking hung in the background of his psyche.

My son's quiet fears were paralleled among clients in my private practice. One of my lesbian clients' family members literally huddled around her when entering a bar on the outskirts of Seattle, where gun racks were common, and acceptance of the gay community was low. Another client, who worked at a high level in the green movement, lamented that "even if we all drove electric cars and recycled daily, it wouldn't be enough to save the planet." His down mood, while influenced by his family-of-origin circumstances, was consciously tied to his sense of helplessness about global warming. He ground his teeth at night and fought depression.

It was 2015–2016. Terrorism was on the rise, climate change had become a regular news topic, gun violence appeared to be making a comeback, and racial tension among white police officers and their black community members was growing—with increasing incidences of black men being shot without any apparent threat. When Rodney King was beaten by LA police in 1991, little did we know that similar racial injustice was on the horizon for Trayvon Martin, Philando Castile, Alton Sterling, and Botham Shem Jean, to name a few of the many black men who've been killed without having physically provoked their non-black police or security guard attackers.

In 2016, the presidential election was well underway, with warring sides campaigning and heated emotions separating friends and families across the country. Anxiety became the number one symptom in my practice. The APA reported in their 2017 "Stress in America" survey that stress had risen from a 4.8 to 5.1 on a ten-point scale among Americans in 2016 alone. In 2018 it had risen to 5.3 regarding Americans' stress about our nation alone.

After Donald Trump was elected, I faced my own unease while trying to heal the nerves of my gay clients, who feared violent discrimination; my immigrant clients, who also feared violence and deportation of family members; clients of color, who felt particularly vulnerable living in a country led by conservative and seemingly racist white leaders; and my female clients, who felt outraged that our president had been chosen despite having admitted to sexually violating women. I also faced paralyzing fear from my chronically-ill clients, whose health insurance (their means of living vs. dying) was threatened. Every time a healthcare bill came up for vote in the Senate, those clients lost sleep. The American Psychological Association reported that the uninsured were significantly more stressed than the insured, and that 56 percent of Americans were worried about changes in government policy that would affect their healthcare.[18]

In addition, many of my clients were experiencing outrage and grief because their families were split politically. They argued about race, sexual orientation, sexism, protection of the environment, etc., upon discovering their mother, father, brother, friend was someone with whom they could no longer identify, someone they didn't care to be in a room with. Clients wept, grieving the loss of the mother they thought they knew or the friend they now missed. I sat in my chair, witnessing the makings of what Ferenczi and Marshall had deemed a fearful attachment to our nation. Many spoke of defecting to Canada or Australia. Some did. Strategies for stress reduction and navigating grief took precedence in my work with clients.

At present, amid the aforementioned and under threat of nuclear war with North Korea, my psychology practice, as well as those of my colleagues, is burgeoning with stress and anxiety. Whether it's a university professor anxious about facilitating a discussion after the Charlottesville riots, in which white supremacists killed a protestor, or a lesbian client afraid her marriage rights will be revoked, or a single father trying to comfort his eleven-year-old daughter about why Kim Jon Ung will likely not hit Seattle with a nuclear missile (when he, himself, is not sure of this), anxiety in relation to our current American circumstances abounds.

I am not saying that stress and worry didn't exist before the year 2000. Of course, they did. There has always been something to worry about. Early settlers lived with the threat of starvation due to drought. Men and women in the 1940s worried their son, brother, father, or lover wouldn't return from Germany in World War II. In the 1980s, some Americans experienced anxiety that the Cold War would erupt into an apocalyptic event. And blacks and other minorities have been repeatedly threatened and discriminated against over many decades. But the question of whether we could rely on our country or planet to be intact was hardly an issue. In addition, our personal relationships were disrupted far less. People moved less, they spoke face to face more and had more time with loved ones, all of which help us be more resilient to stress. What we are experiencing now isn't like other stressful events in our history. We seem to have more chronic stress and less resilience to it.

Teens and Stress

"We certainly do not understand why it is harder to make plans with friends on weekends than it is to buy an automatic or semiautomatic weapon."

—Emma Gonzalez,
Marjory Stoneman Douglas High School
Parkland, Florida

Perhaps a clearer window into stress in the US is through the lives of our teenagers. School shootings have become common and 75 percent of Z gens say mass shootings are a significant source of their stress. Teen suicide shot up 4 percent between 2009 and 2015. Apparently, teens who use electronic devices for five or more hours a day are 66 percent more likely to have suicidal thoughts or actions than teens who only used devices for one hour per day.[19] Do you know any teen who only uses his or her device for one hour a day? I don't. On top of that, the daily use of social media rose from 58 percent to 87 percent between 2009 and 2015, and those daily users were 14 percent more likely to be depressed than less-frequent users of social media. In case you didn't know, depression is considered both a cause and a result of stress in humans.

I remember watching on the news one day students from the Marjorie Stoneman High School shooting in Florida cry as lawmakers in their state turned down a ban on assault weapons. Just one week prior, these students were traumatized by a mass shooting at their school that killed seventeen of their classmates. As a result, the surviving students felt the need to take on gun violence themselves and bussed to the state's capital to push for bans on certain weapons, like the AR-15 that killed their friends. This mature response to a

17

horror no kid should have to go through is an example of how overwhelmed our adolescents are today.

I spoke with psychology professor and researcher Tom Plante, PhD, at Santa Clara University about the phenomenon of rising stress among college students. Dr. Plante has been teaching psychology at the university for twenty-four years and, along with Doug Oman of UC Berkeley and Carl E. Thoreson of Stanford University, is one of the founders of the Spirituality and Health Institute at SCU.

I walked across Santa Clara's beautiful mission campus, enjoying the sunshine and palm trees, and noticed how peaceful I felt. Arriving at Dr. Plante's office, I found him hastily eating his lunch, knowing I was due to interview him before his next class. Friendly and passionate, Plante spoke candidly in his East Coast accent about campus life and how, despite the peace and beauty I had just experienced, the students were struggling.

"These kids come to us fried, and it's very concerning," he stated. "They're anxious, they're depressed, they're struggling with ADHD and OCD, they're worried about the world."

Plante maintained that in his last term, one-third of his two classes had accommodations. Academic accommodations are special educational resources for students with "disabilities" such as learning differences, attention problems, and even psychological problems like anxiety and depression. The percentage of students who need accommodations is up from previous decades, and Dr. Plante attributes it to a conglomeration of factors such as attention issues caused by screen addiction and the No Child Left Behind law, which aims to hold schools accountable for children's academic performance by testing students. Some maintain this has resulted in "teaching to the test" and having kids follow an educational rubric, which doesn't allow for individual learning styles. It can put a lot of pressure on kids by defining for them how to do their work. Then, there is pressure from parents who fear their kids won't succeed in life if they don't do well academically.

"If you don't do well in everything, including taking tons of extra-curricular and AP courses and starting an orphanage in a third-world country on the side, you'll never get into a decent college," Plante intentionally exaggerates, making the point that kids these days feel they have to overachieve just to make it in life.

"When those kids come to us on the college level, they're not prepared for college because they're not prepared to think on their own. When you assign a reflection paper, they need to know how many pages, what size font, how many references…this has become our culture." And seems to be, in part, a result of teaching to the test.

Ted Grover, high school media teacher for the Oakland Unified School District and now the Richmond Public School District agrees. "A lot of what we've done in education is we've told kids what to do and how to think so now they don't think for themselves." Grover endorses a Social Constructionism Model that promotes collaboration and takes a classroom from being teacher-centered to student-centered. "It makes them stronger, more confident and they have extremely strong interpersonal connections as a result of this model," something Grover's urban, at-risk youth particularly need these days as economic hardship and gentrification has taken a toll on family and neighborhood communities. Grover teaches in the number one school in the Bay Area for ethnic diversity. It's not necessarily racial tension, but economic tension that creates a challenge in his classroom. "Often, the low-income kids who come from horrible middle schools are the ones that act out because they feel left out. They may not be able to keep up or even read something on the computer that the more affluent kids can read. You've got to know the trauma a kid brings with him into the classroom. You have to be open. You can't judge them. You have to establish trust, so they'll learn the classroom is safe for them."

Plante also cites the research that addresses social media (a phenomenon that almost all our adolescents participate in daily).

"The more people are engaged in social media, particularly passive social media, the more likely they are to become depressed and have these anxious and affective issues," he said.

He sees firsthand the support for Jean Twenge's research findings mentioned above.

"You walk through the campus and everyone's on their phones."

"It's a disconnected connection," Grover states. But in his community, there is an upside to phone use. "It also opens up *my* connection to my students as I text with them a lot," insinuating the relationship-building aspect of this form of communication.

The solution to the problem, Plante says, is "social engineering." That is, building in limitations for ourselves and our teens so that we are less impacted by screen or social media use but can still benefit from them. In other words, we'll have to intervene on our habits with more than just willpower which I'll discuss along the way and again in Chapter Ten. Plante's work with the Spirituality and Health Institute, which has well-researched preventative and responsive solutions to our postmillennial stress as well as Oakland's implementation of Restorative Justice, a program aimed to promote community support and reduce school suspensions, expulsions and recidivism rates for youth crime, demonstrate organized effort to make life go better for our teens and young adults. In addition, Grover's cited Social Constructionism Model and another program called "Trauma Informed" are additional approaches to help raise kids up vs. lose them to an economically and digitally-challenged world.

What's the Media Got to Do with It?

"Getting your news from Twitter is like asking a cat for directions."
—Andy Borowitz

Greek philosopher Epictetus said, "People are not disturbed by things, but by the view they take of them." This statement describes the phenomenon of present-day media on our psyches. In the 1940s, there was radio and there were newspapers. People usually only heard the news if they purposefully turned on their radio and listened to it or bought a paper and read it. In addition, news reporters were trained to be neutral. Whether they achieved it or not is up for debate, but that was the overall aim.

Today, access to the news is at our fingertips. Our computer screens flash headlines when we click on our browsers to go online, our phones notify us with the latest news stories around the clock, and even when we take a break to exercise at the gym or have a meal out, televisions are often attached to the treadmill or the restaurant wall, keeping us informed of the day's events.

Comments about the news abound on Facebook and Twitter and, as a result of the Russian hacking into these two platforms, we are now learning how vulnerable we can be to the influence of social media. The investigation into Russia's meddling in our 2016 election found that Russian hackers created Facebook and Twitter accounts, spreading falsified information that would potentially sway Americans from voting for Hillary Clinton.

There has been a lot of talk lately about the responsibility the media has in reporting the news. Some news channels or sites are deemed biased, favoring certain pieces of news and coloring others to fit the news station's personal views. In addition, incessant reporting on myriad shooting rampages can sometimes glorify the shooter, unintentionally conditioning some criminals to believe that orchestrating a massacre can lead to "fame." What, when, and how should journalists and news agencies report? What is their responsibility? While free press is a value we enjoy as a democracy, and the media can uncover truths that would have otherwise been hidden from us, it can also saturate us.

Recently, I ran into a friend at Starbucks on one of the mornings that Hurricane Irma was bearing down on the Caribbean and threatening Florida.

"I'm so stressed," he said.

As I had momentarily forgotten about hurricane news, I asked him why he was so stressed.

"Because of the hurricane! I can't stop watching the news. I'm one of those people who watches it nonstop, you know."

"Well, maybe you should stop watching it," I suggested.

He just shrugged.

One study, conducted by Massachusetts General Hospital and Harvard Medical School, found that children were vulnerable to PTSD symptoms and full-blown PTSD diagnoses after indirect exposure to 9/11. In other words, children under ten who watched television news coverage of the 9/11 attacks were more prone to PTSD symptoms and diagnoses than children who didn't watch it. Additionally, this study showed that even a small percentage of adults were prone to PTSD diagnoses after watching the 9/11 coverage.[20]

The key may be simple: monitor yourself and your children. Use the news to stay informed so you can make educated decisions about voting, participating, or staying safe. Turn off the news if it makes you agitated or anxious. If the news is motivating, it has done its job; but if it causes increasing distress, it may be counterproductive.

Smartphones, Laptops, and Tablets—Oh, My!

"The brain does not discern between real or perceived threats, and artificially intense stimulation from electronic screen media produces a psychological fight-or-flight reaction, regardless of content."

—Victoria Dunckley, MD

"I don't like this forest," Dorothy says in The Wizard of Oz. *"It's dark and creepy."*

"I think it's going to get darker before it gets lighter," the Scarecrow replies.
"Do…do you suppose we'll meet any wild animals?" Dorothy asks.

The Wizard of Oz is a movie that has touched generations of hearts. As is true for most films, it's riddled with metaphors. From a psychoanalytic perspective, the dark forest represents the unknown, the unconscious or *shadow*. According to Swiss psychiatrist Carl Jung, the shadow is the aspect of an individual or culture that has been repressed. It typically consists of primitive impulses and emotions, such as greed, anger, and hatred. It usually encompasses the aspects of oneself that we'd rather not acknowledge. Sometimes, we project these aspects onto other people: "He's so selfish. I can't stand him." This may be a reflection of the part of ourselves we cannot tolerate, and so we project it onto another human being.

What, you may ask, has the shadow got to do with technology? As is the case with many inventions and discoveries, we tend to get so excited about the novelty or power of something that we don't consider it may have a dark side. The atom bomb, for example, seemed like a powerful and effective solution to ending WWII, but once it hit, the world stood in shock at its destruction. Smoking seemed like a good idea when cigarettes first hit the United States in the 1800s. By the 1900s, cigarette sales were in the billions, skyrocketing during WWI and WWII. It wasn't until 1964, when the surgeon general reported that cigarettes were a health hazard, that tobacco ads became government regulated. Whoops—smoking can kill us, we discovered.

Similarly, Steve Jobs proudly presented us with the iPhone in 2007. He walked onto the stage at the Moscone Center in San Francisco and said to his cheering audience, "We're going to make some history together today." And history he made. Between 2007 and 2016, iPhone sales reached one billion dollars, with close to one hundred million users in the US alone. I am one of them. Apple recently became the first American company to be worth a trillion dollars.

What Jobs may not have realized was that while his device made emailing, banking, shopping, and listening to music much more accessible, it would eventually become an object of addiction, the source of anxiety, and, as was recently announced on CNN, the possible cause of depression in some of its users.[21] Not only are parents scrambling to figure out ways to prevent brain dysregulation in their kids due to electromagnetic emissions and overstimulation from smartphones, but even Apple investors pressured the media giant to install tools that can help parents regulate their kids' phone use. One adult client of mine noticed that she repeatedly and compulsively looked at her phone several times an hour without knowing what she was looking for. Her anxiety had increased and her insomnia had gotten worse, despite diligent work in therapy. We switched our focus from her family-of-origin trauma to her phone addiction. I worked with her as I would an addict, and she began to improve.

Not everyone has the awareness, discipline, time, or money for therapy. Others aren't necessarily addicted to screen use, but they still suffer as they move from repeatedly checking their phone, to working on their laptop, to surfing their tablet at night. They aren't aware of the technology shadow: that chronic exposure to screens is creating physiological and psychological stress. And, like Scarecrow in *The Wizard of Oz* says, "I think it's going to get darker before it gets lighter." But, don't worry, I have dedicated an entire chapter to technology, as well as solutions to the problem, as I believe its role in our current stress levels has been severely underestimated.

2

ATTACHMENT THEORY AND RESILIENCE TO STRESS: THE PROBLEM AND THE SOLUTION

"We make the world better by making people safer."

—Stephen Porges, PhD

at-tach-ment (in the context of attachment theory) *(noun):* a long-lasting psychological connection with a meaningful person of which the quality of attachment has a critical effect on physical and emotional development and has been linked to psychological and neurological well-being.

When I was at the tender age of one, I had the following experience: *I am alone in what seems like an empty, gray space, the color of light ash. It is quiet, and the light is dim. I can't see very well. I sense danger and feel helpless and frightened. I cry out and a rescuer appears. I cannot adequately see him in the low light, but I feel the containment and safety of loving arms—arms I would later know as my father's. He picks me up and I see a gray ceiling swirl around a bright spot that wanders in and out of view. I know now that bright spot was the ceiling light that shone above my crib. Suddenly, I am no longer on the merry-go-round with the ceiling, but am right-side-up, looking at a wall as my father holds me in his arms. Being righted and in the arms of my father, I feel safe and warm. Comfort sets in. I'm no longer scared.*

It is rare to have memories this young, but it is one that has stayed with me throughout my life. Recalling it sends me back to palpable fear when I awoke to the sense of separation, followed by comfort when I remember my father picking me up. A soothing parental response to a baby's distress is one of the vital experiences a child needs to build what psychologists call *secure attachment.*

What is a *secure attachment,* and what does it have to do with stress in the US? To be securely attached means that you have likely had a consistent and comforting relationship with another human being over time that helps you feel safe and secure in yourself and in the world. When we are babies, we rely on our caregivers (otherwise known as *attachment figures*) for consistent, soothing, and engaged responses. If we get these responses, we internalize the comfort and security the relationship with the attachment figures give us and can feel safe and secure when separated from the attachment figures. Later, as adolescents and adults, we are better equipped to handle stressful events because we've internalized the safe experience of the attachment figures.

The attachment process doesn't end there, though. Secure or insecure attachments continue when we form relationships as adults, particularly romantic relationships. And, as I explained in Chapter One, we can also form a secure or insecure attachment to our nation. Why are these attachments related to our stress levels? Because secure attachments build resilience (sometimes referred to as grit) and resilience helps us handle stress.

Hang with me while I explain the history of attachment theory. It's an important concept to understand and central to the theme of this book. After all, the more we can find ways to become securely attached, the better we'll be able to handle the cultural stress we face today.

In the 1950s, two important figures of psychology entered the main stage: Psychoanalyst John Bowlby, whose groundbreaking article "Maternal Care and Mental Health" in 1950 paved the way for attachment theory, and psychologist Harry Harlow, whose famous (yet controversial) maternal deprivation experiment with baby monkeys demonstrated the importance of early parental nurturing.

Harlow's 1958 experiment, albeit unethical in its use of animals, deprived rhesus monkeys of contact with their biological mother and placed them with inanimate, "surrogate" mothers. One mother was made of wire, the other of soft terrycloth. While both "mothers" had bottles of milk attached to them where the baby monkeys could get their food, the terrycloth "mother" had the added benefit of being soft and, therefore, easier to cuddle with. What Harlow discovered was that, given the choice, the babies who fed on the wire mother would go to the cloth mother for comfort, and the babies who fed on the cloth mother would stay with the cloth mother, indicating the monkeys' need for comfort exceeded being satiated by milk.[22]

In an additional experiment, when the baby monkeys were exposed to distressing sights and sounds, those without a surrogate mother shrieked and rocked back and forth, attempting to soothe themselves, while those with a surrogate mother cuddled against "her" and eventually calmed. He also compared the physical health of monkeys raised by wire vs. cloth mothers and found that the babies raised by the wire mothers had soft stools, indicating digestive problems, likely caused by stress. With these various experiments, Harlow made the case that a child's psychological health was dependent on early nurturance in addition to basic physiological needs, such as hunger, being met.

Bowlby expanded on Harlow's basic premise that babies need nurturance beyond the bottle by demonstrating through his own (more humane) work that a child's emotional security was heavily influenced by whether his caregivers gave him emotionally attuned responses. In essence, Bowlby theorized that children developed either secure or insecure attachments depending on their psychological environment. If babies and toddlers were responded to lovingly and consistently, they usually developed secure attachments. If babies and toddlers were responded to harshly or inconsistently, they exhibited overly anxious behavior when the caregiver disappeared and continued agitation even after the caregiver reappeared.[23] One could say these babies were *stressed*.

Bowlby's successor, Mary Ainsworth, built on his research with her own. Ainsworth is well known for her famous "Strange Situation" experiment, in which a one-year-old is brought to a playroom with his mother. The baby is then exposed to a stranger who enters the room, and then left with the stranger, temporarily, when the mother exits the room. She returns moments later. Ainsworth observed that some children exhibited extremely anxious behavior when they were presented with the stranger and/or separated from the parent but were *resistant* to the parent's soothing when the parent finally reappeared. Others didn't appear distressed about the stranger's presence when the parent was there, nor when the parent left the room (deemed unusual). These children *avoided* seeking comfort from the parent when she would reappear.

In contrast to children who demonstrated secure attachments, children demonstrating *anxious-resistant* or *avoidant* attachments were children whose parents, consciously or not, were unattuned to their needs. In other words, these parents tended to be inconsistent, rejecting, or even engulfing of their babies and toddlers. Thus,

Ainsworth identified three main attachment styles: secure, avoidant, and ambivalent (or anxious-resistant).

Additional research defined the anxious attachment styles further, breaking the avoidant-attachment into two categories: *dismissive-avoidant* and *fearful-avoidant* (or avoidant and ambivalent) and renaming the anxious attachment style as anxious-preoccupied. While the dismissive-avoidant tends to deny the need for closeness and avoid it, the fearful-avoidant (ambivalent) wants and yet is afraid of emotional closeness. Finally, the anxious-preoccupied is someone who hungers for emotional love to validate her value.

As research in attachment theory continued, Ainsworth's colleague, Mary Main, discovered and named a fourth type of attachment: *disorganized.* This attachment style was thought to come about as a result of a highly unpredictable, unavailable, or abusive environment in which the child did not feel safe and could not predict the parent's response to his/her emotional world. The child's response to the parent was variable. In other words, sometimes he would run and hide, other times he would rock back and forth, seemingly to soothe his fear, and other times he would seek comfort. As a result of the terrifying circumstances of unpredictable parental behavior, people with disorganized attachment have difficulty trusting others and often have short-term relationships they try to control in order to avoid re-traumatization.

If you want to find out your attachment style, take this simple quiz below to get an idea of what category you may be in.

Following, are four general relationship styles that people often report. Place a checkmark next to the letter corresponding to the style that best describes you or is closest to the way you are.

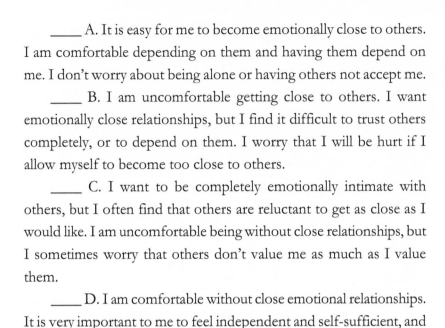

_____ A. It is easy for me to become emotionally close to others. I am comfortable depending on them and having them depend on me. I don't worry about being alone or having others not accept me.

_____ B. I am uncomfortable getting close to others. I want emotionally close relationships, but I find it difficult to trust others completely, or to depend on them. I worry that I will be hurt if I allow myself to become too close to others.

_____ C. I want to be completely emotionally intimate with others, but I often find that others are reluctant to get as close as I would like. I am uncomfortable being without close relationships, but I sometimes worry that others don't value me as much as I value them.

_____ D. I am comfortable without close emotional relationships. It is very important to me to feel independent and self-sufficient, and I prefer not to depend on others or have others depend on me.

Bartholomew, K. & Horowitz, L. M. (1991). Attachment styles among young adults: A test of a four-category model. *Journal of Personality and Social Psychology*, 61, 226–244.

If you chose A, you likely have a secure attachment style. If you chose B, you likely have an ambivalent attachment style. If you chose C, you likely have an anxious-preoccupied attachment, and if you chose D, you likely have a dismissive-avoidant attachment. The more securely attached an individual is, the more resilient to stress he is. A person with a secure attachment is less likely to ruminate or isolate when faced with the loss of a loved one. He is more likely to seek appropriate support from others while still able to soothe his own pain. Therefore, securely attached people weather hardship better,[24,25] are less likely to get anxious or depressed,[26,27,28] are better able to sleep,[29,30,31,32,33] have more successful relationships,[34] and a better sense of well-being.[35] When you have a secure attachment style your stress is more manageable.

Now, no relationship in any era is perfectly attuned. Parents get tired, frustrated, and short-fused, sometimes rendering an impatient response to the baby. Married couples argue and hurt each other's feelings. Nations get invaded and fail to protect their residents at times. If the attachment relationship is threatened or disrupted by this kind of mis-attunement, not all is lost. In the case of the baby, the attachment figure can *repair* the mis-attunement once he sees the baby's distress by soothing the baby with compassionate sounds such as "ohhh," or with touch, like a tender stroke of the head. These responses signal "I'm sorry, and I'm here" to the baby. In the case of the couple, the one partner can offer a genuine apology to the other and empathize with how he hurt his partner's feelings. In the case of the nation, the government can take measures to protect its residents from harm and defend itself against potential attack, especially when a traumatic event has occurred. In all cases, repair demonstrates that while disruptions or misunderstandings occur, things can be made better. One can feel safe and secure again.

The repair part of an attachment relationship is key, as it instills resilience in both parties. When anxiety abounded among US residents after the shock and terror of 9/11, a disruption in our sense of safety in the US occurred. Subsequently, many suffered from anxiety, and some were scared to fly on planes. But, when the government implemented safety measures to increase security at airports and on airplanes, residents' anxiety eventually ebbed, and many learned flying could be okay again. Some degree of repair occurred.

But often these days, any repair we attempt (either nationally or personally) seems to be overshadowed by continued disruption and prevention of secure attachments. Think texting vs. talking, social media exchanges vs. gatherings, parents too busy to look their kids in the eye, racial discrimination, gun violence, and the fact that our planet is dying. As illustrated in Chapter One, these disruptions in secure attachment are growing, and therefore, our sense of security and resilience to stress is suffering. As Americans, we are in a time in which stress is high and resilience is low.[36]

Attachment Relationships and Brain Development:
The Beginning of Resilience to Stress

"The face is the picture of the mind with the eyes as its interpreter."

—Cicero

In 1989, at the urging of Congress, the National Institute for Mental Health, and the National Institute for Neurological Disorders and Stroke, President George Bush signed a declaration stating the 1990s would be deemed the "decade of the brain." The initiative funded researchers and early childhood development programs to study brain development. As a result, the field of psychology began to look intently at the relationship between attachment theory and the brain. Allan Shore, PhD was one of the pioneers in this area of interest, paving the way for subsequent researchers to build on his postulations.

In 1994, Schore began extensive research aiming to understand the integration of biology and psychology, resulting in a field of study that we now know as interpersonal neurobiology—a term coined by Dan Siegel MD. In his groundbreaking book *Affect Regulation and the Repair of the Self,* Shore states that the bidirectional relationship between the child and its parent can have direct and enduring effects on the child's brain development and behavior. Wow! In fact, "the development of a baby's nervous system is inextricably tied to its parents' physical and emotional responses, which can later inform a person's relationship to stress," Schore says. And he continues, "stable attachment bonds that transmit high levels of positive affect (smiling, for example) are vitally important for the infant's neurobiological development."[37] What Schore is talking about here is the phenomenon of the infant/parent "gaze." That is, when babies and their caregivers communicate via their facial expressions and vocal sounds in lieu of words, attunement happens, and brain growth occurs.

Studies show that a caregiver's pupils will dilate when looking at a baby and that babies smile in response to caregiver pupil dilation[38]. In other words, the caregiver's physiology is interacting with the babies on an unconscious level. That is pretty cool and pretty powerful! Schore states, "The mother's emotionally expressive face is by far the most potent visual stimulus in the infant's environment." Why? Because the baby's right hemisphere grows as a result of looking at the mother's facial expression. How? The mother's right hemisphere (which processes emotional information nonverbally) imprints on the baby's right cortex when she smiles or looks gleefully surprised, as an example.

As I discussed in the previous section, inevitably, something will go awry in this infant/caregiver exchange. For example, the phone may ring, and the parent may move out of sight to answer it, causing the baby distress. If the caregiver returns to the baby and soothes its distress, then he can repair the mis-attunement. It's like getting off-step briefly in a tango. You and your partner may feel your heart skip as your feet are no longer coordinated, risking confusion, or worse, a fall. But, as a dancer, you can quickly get back on track and glide in sync across the dance floor, thus repairing the momentary derailment. Getting back in step repairs the otherwise estranging moment. In the case of the caregiver and the baby (and the dancers, for that matter), repair or realignment teaches one that negative experiences can be overcome, and therefore, emotional resilience gets established.

But what happens when repair doesn't occur? This is when a baby is at risk for developing an insecure or disorganized attachment and possibly at risk for problematic brain development. I spoke with Mona Delahooke, PhD, a Los Angeles clinical psychologist and the author of *Social and Emotional Development in Early Intervention: A Skills Guide for Working with Children*. Dr. Delahooke works with children who are struggling with emotional and behavioral problems, usually due to neurological issues, such as autism spectrum disorders, oppositional-defiant disorders, and/or attention deficit disorders, to name a few. Spending most of her sessions on the floor in tactile play with kids and parents, Dr. Delahooke emphasizes the importance of the child/caregiver relationship in reducing and even healing the child's problematic symptoms.

Dr. Delahooke works with her child-clients and their parents by helping parents emotionally attune to and regulate their children organically. "I believe the foundation of mental health is for children to co-regulate their physiological state with their caregivers [because] co-regulation of state leads to self-regulation later in life."[39] This approach echoes attachment theory's postulations that our attunement to each other (our understanding and acceptance of our individual differences, as well as in-person, eye-to-eye communication) is what reduces stress, thereby increasing our brain health and regulating our autonomic nervous system.

My older son was particularly sensitive to loud noises when he was young. You wouldn't know it now the way he cranks his guitar amp, but, when he was two, he would run out of the room when the thunder sounded on the *Winnie the Pooh* show, overwhelmed by the noise coming through the television. Had I discounted his experience by saying there was nothing to be afraid of, it was just a show, I would not have attuned to his experience. Lucky for him, this was one of those moments in which I was attuned—I wasn't always—and learned to turn down the volume a bit and cover my ears, too, when we knew the thunder was coming.

It is amazing to think that we have such an effect on one another. The fact that my nervous system (if balanced) can help balance my baby's is extraordinary. To see Dr. Delahooke in action will make anyone want to be in her company. She interacts with her clients with unwavering presence, using her voice, face, and body to mirror the client's sensory experience of the world, thus demonstrating to parents what it looks like to attune to their children. She is no different outside the therapy room. Engaged, positive, hopeful, and seeing the potential in everyone, Dr. Delahooke makes you feel seen and safe in her presence. Remember, *feeling safe and seen are the seeds of a healthy attachment formation, and secure attachments reduce stress.*

But today, stressed-out parents spend a fair amount of time with their eyes glued to a screen, not to their babies as they try to respond to their boss's text while breastfeeding or get to that string of emails instead of playing hide and seek. And, in order to not frustrate the baby or toddler, electronic devices are often placed in their hands, too, casually known as the "electronic babysitter." *If people like Dr. Delahooke are only found in therapy offices, what is this doing to the next generation of brains? Are the Z-gens learning more about avoidance than intimacy?* Let's look further.

How American Culture Disrupts Secure Attachment

"I looked back on the past and recalled my peoples' old ways, but they were not living that way anymore. They were traveling the black road, everybody for himself, with little rules of his own."

—Black Elk

35

We used to live in tribes and close to the earth. This gave people cohesion with one another, safety in numbers, a sense of belonging, and surely aided in resilience to stress. The above quote from Black Elk refers to the time when Native American tribes were dismantled by white men. I use it because I believe we're living in a time in which our attachments to each other and our nation are at risk of being dismantled yet again. When it comes down to it, what we have in this life is each other. We need each other not only to thrive but to survive.

In the 2017 September issue of the *Monitor on Psychology,* Kirsten Weir looks at what fosters a child's resilience (or ability to thrive amidst stress). Resilience is defined, in part, by your ability to regulate emotion, exercise self-control, and call upon internal motivation and external resources. And, one of the clearest determinants of resilience is a child's relationship with her tribe, especially her parent. If a child has a secure attachment to her primary caregiver (usually the mother, but sometimes the father, and, in some cases, an older sibling), the relationship's reliability and nurturance can help protect the child against adverse effects of stress.

It makes sense. If we can rely on a stable family or community, we feel emotionally protected and safer. We are more likely to exercise optimism and make healthy decisions. But what is most noteworthy about the importance of healthy attachments, particularly between parent and child, is that the child's brain has a better chance of healthy development. And if the child's brain is healthy, it is capable of regulating emotion, cognition, and behavior which allows the child (and eventual adult) to handle stress.

While attachment researchers make a strong case for the relationship between secure attachment and resilience, it turns out one's relationship with his or her primary caregiver may not be enough to thrive in life these days. Suniya Luthar, PhD, a research scientist and psychology professor at Arizona State University, reported surprising findings in 2017. In two of her articles, "Adolescents from upper middle class communities: Substance misuse and addiction across early adulthood" and "Youth in High-Achieving Schools: Challenges to Mental Health and Direction for Evidence-Based Interventions," Luthar et al. report on the fact that youth in upper-middle-class families are 1.5 to 2.5 times more like to suffer from anxiety, depression, and substance abuse issues than the national normative sample of youth! These findings are contrary to popular belief that upper-middle-class kids are more protected against mental health and substance use issues because of the financial and educational opportunities they have.

Particularly interesting is that Luthar does not attribute these upper-middle-class problems to insecure attachment to caregivers. Nor does she attribute the problem to poor relationships with school administration and faculty. Instead, she blames these skyrocketing rates of mental instability and substance abuse on our culture in the United States. Specifically, she talks about how "more is better" in the United States—how there is constant pressure to make a lot of money and have a lot of material things and get a lot of accolades for one's achievements.

"You see, if your sense of self-worth gets tied into how much you can accomplish...two things happen. One is, if you don't accomplish, you feel small, inadequate, lousy. The other is, you live in a state of fear of not achieving.... If I can tell myself I'm a good person because I'm a good mother, a good friend, that's one thing. If I tell myself I'm a good person to the degree that I get that next grant or I become famous or I receive these accolades, I'm living in fear. These are things that are not as much in my control as are things like being a good mother or being a good friend. So, living in this constant state of tension and fear—if I don't achieve, who will I be?—is something that puts us in a state of anxiety…and a state of depression," reports Luthar to APA's Audrey Hamilton.

Luthar goes on to explain that both kids and parents subsequently learn to self-medicate the anxiety and depression through drugs and alcohol. Could our opioid epidemic and high suicide rate be due, in part, to the pain of perceived failure?

Perhaps it's like an infection run amok. It starts with the unconscious identification we have as Americans that we are the greatest, most powerful nation on earth. The "bigger is better" concept gets played out in the media and in advertising, bleeds into the minds of parents, schools, kids, and, before you know it, we are all caught up in a vicious cycle—a *Race to Nowhere,* as Vicki Abeles's aptly titled documentary illustrates.[40]

Race to Nowhere supports Luthar's research. Through interviews with kids, parents, school administrators, and faculty, the filmmakers try to make sense of why our youth are so stressed out despite the fact that many of these kids appear to come from loving, stable households. It appears that Professor Plante is right: kids are subject to the "rubric" and the worry about not getting into a decent college. They are overscheduled and over-focused on grades. Some even commit suicide because they fear they aren't good enough. Indeed, when I asked my then thirteen-year-old and his friends what stresses them out the most, they all responded similarly: "pressure to do well in school," "getting good grades so I can get a good job," "making sure I get all my homework done so my parents don't get mad."

In addition to this cultural pressure is the phenomenon of the smartphone. Children, teens, and parents are glued to their phones these days, greatly reducing that powerful eye contact Schore talks about as key to brain development. How many parents have you witnessed busily attending to tasks while their toddlers zone out on phones or tablets? How many parents or babysitters have you seen barely aware of their baby's emotional or physical experience as they walk down the street with the stroller in one hand and a smartphone in the other? How many teens have you noticed zombied out on devices while parents shop, work, or surf the net? Research shows that the more we engage in digital communication, the less able we are to develop intimate relationships. Are we becoming a desensitized society that seems to care less about each other's well-being?

Sam Keen, author of the 1986 book *Faces of the Enemy,* wrote about our capacity to dehumanize each other by projecting the darker aspects of ourselves onto people and cultures we don't really know, like Nazi Germany did with Jews. As a result, we make the other the enemy and give ourselves reign to demean and attack them. This kind of insensitivity and projection could be increasing, not just between nations (as Keen pointed out), but among each other on a personal level. In other words, if our face-to-face communication is decreased by the digital age, intimate and secure attachments don't even get a fair chance to develop. As a result, we are more disconnected from one another and, therefore, more likely to hurt each other. Think cyberbullying. Think building walls. Think Muslim travel bans.

If parents rely on devices to babysit their children, and if robot babysitters are just around the corner (author Sherry Turkle indicates such a practice isn't far off), could human-device and human-robot interaction as a replacement to human-human interaction make us more callous and, therefore, less likely to help and protect one another from harm? In addition, are we actually causing vs. relieving stress by allowing devices and robots help us out in life?

The film *Screenagers: Growing up in the Digital Age*[41] creatively tells the story of how digital devices are affecting our children and how parents are shooting in the dark to intervene. With no preparation or training on how to prevent screen addiction (which, researchers are now finding, causes problems in our physical and mental health and is possibly changing our brains for the worse)[42] parents' responses to their children's screen use can range from aggressive to resigned. Most of us scramble for interventions, many of which don't work.

As if these cultural influences aren't enough for us to combat, the ever-present anxiety of gun violence, particularly in schools, impacts kids and parents today. With no federal government increases on gun control, kids are so worried about shootings that they, themselves, organized and executed a DC protest called March for Our Lives on March 24, 2018, drawing almost a million participants. Approximately four hundred cities worldwide held sister events. Grover, the high school teacher from the Bay Area, and a former teacher in the Oakland School District said he's lost six of his students to gun violence. Teaching in communities where gangs are prevalent, Grover says that many of the kids walk the halls with pictures of family members who were shot to death around their necks. Each year Grover has family members walking the graduation stage for their son or brother who was killed, usually in gang-related violence.

Similarly, many ethnic groups and immigrants residing in the US feel more threatened than supported by this country as they fear attack or deportation under the current administration. Even the children of immigrant parents who were born in the US and know no other home, plea with the government not to expel them to countries in which they've never lived. At Grover's former school, ICE sat on either end of the school waiting for parents to drop or pick up their kids in order to nab any undocumented parents. "This is the biggest stress of my undocumented kids—the fear their parents will be taken from them," Grover says. One could say that a political *faces-of-the-enemy* situation, in which minorities are seen as the bad guys, makes these ethnic groups particularly vulnerable in today's America.

Are we feeling less protected and more estranged from our own country? Do we feel we have to protect ourselves in the absence of protective parental figures in government? Psychologist and attachment theorist David Wallin, PhD, would say yes. In an interview I held with him, Wallin spoke to the unsettledness he witnessed in his patients and community after the divisive 2016 election. "There was the election of a bully, the election of a sexual predator. What that has meant for many is that at the head of our nation is a bad attachment figure," says Wallin. He goes on to say, "This has resulted in an insecure or unresolved attachment to our nation." Both Wallin and I concur that anxiety symptoms about national issues have risen in our patients since the 2016 election.

While decreasing connections with one another and disruptions in secure attachment may be a significant problem right now, it is fixable. Remember how healthy adult relationships can change a person's childhood attachment experience? The same can be true nationally. Let's find out how we can make use of attachment theory to repair our seemingly damaged attachment to our nation and how a repaired attachment can help us cope with stress.

Repairing an Insecure Attachment to Our Nation
(And to Each Other)

Coming Together

Interviewed recently by news anchor Chris Hayes of MSNBC, Jane Fonda said, "Hope is activism." What did she mean by that? Well, she was talking about how when we, as residents of the US, band together in order to speak our minds or protest a threat to our safety and security, we can make a change. We clearly saw this in the 1960s, when Martin Luther King organized the peaceful march to Selma in order to give black people the rights they deserved. We also saw it when protests abounded after the Trump administration attempted to ban visitors from predominantly Muslim countries. Americans across the country showed up at airports to speak out against such an abandoning gesture to our fellow global citizens. As a result of that outcry, judges in Washington state, Hawaii, and Maryland all administered orders to prevent the ban and won.

The students of Stoneman Douglas High School in Florida are another example of how activism doesn't have to be attacking. After seventeen students and staff members were gunned down and another seventeen injured, the remaining students took to the streets, organizing a nationwide march and pleading for stricter gun laws. Plans of the march went viral and drew millions to the streets, including 800,000 protesters in DC alone. That is a phenomenal coming together of American residents, inspired by teenagers in the face of tragedy. While change can be slow, there have been at least six reported changes in gun legislation and financial support of the NRA as a result of this massive show of activism.

Not everyone is into showing up at airports on a weekday afternoon or marching in gun law protests. In fact, many people believe Trump's bans and the current gun laws don't need protesting. It's these very differences in opinions that our country needs to recall how to navigate. But if we're afraid of one another (an insecure attachment), how do we change that?

Honor Our Commonalities

We need to find our commonalities as humans. We all suffer. We all get scared. Perhaps we start with that concept. Often when a patient is fuming about a friend who wronged her, I work to help her understand the friend's behavior in the context of his suffering. I'm not talking about condoning the friend's behavior, but about having empathy for its context as a way to prevent acts of revenge that only serve to keep an adversarial relationship active and stress chronic.

Releasing judgment long enough to truly listen to the other side is imperative. Somewhere beneath the defenses of attacking rhetoric is a vulnerable being. During a visit to school-aged kids, Thich Nhat Hanh was asked what to do when another kid makes fun of you (essentially, bullies you.) He replied that the student should look the attacker in the eye and tell him she sees he is suffering and is sorry. That is not a usual response. But think about it. Once you honor the tender underbelly of another human, despite their defenses, you no longer feel under their thumb. You are repairing divisiveness.

School-Based Restorative Justice

Another vehicle for repairing disrupted or insecure attachment is to work with schools. In my hometown of Oakland, California, restorative educational justice is now the heart of the district's disciplinary system. Restorative justice is the well-researched practice of responding to school violations by teaching relationship-building through empathy, respect, responsibility, and inclusivity. It encompasses three tiers of prevention and intervention: Tier 1) relationship-building among the administrators, staff and students through what are called circle groups—deep and open exchanges based on indigenous practices that value inclusivity, Tier 2) non-punitive responses to harm that seek to heal and repair the harm, by nonjudgmentally understanding the root cause of the violating behavior and its impact on the one harmed, while holding the one who has harmed accountable, and Tier 3) supporting re-entry to the school if, indeed, a student is expelled or goes to jail. Oakland is known for a large, economically-disadvantaged, minority student population. Crimes occur often in populations like these, as stress is high and emotional and economic support is low. Prior to 2006, test scores were historically low in the Oakland public schools, while suspensions were high.

Once the restorative educational justice system got underway in 2006 at Oakland's Cole Middle School, it was clear that this approach to tweens and teens was transformative for our youth. By 2009, suspensions had dropped by 81 percent and expulsions were nonexistent. GPAs were way up. Now, Oakland's entire public-school system has adopted the program and continues to boast statistics like these. Teiahsha Bankhead, Executive Director of Restorative Justice for Oakland Youth, explained the program's success in an interview I had with her: "Oakland has teachers who don't see these youth as 'those people' but as 'our people.' This is true for both teachers of color and white teachers. There is this sense that these kids are *all of our children* and we're willing to go outside the box to reach for them."

In other words, restorative justice is about truly healing harm vs. simply punishing the one who harmed. Bankhead goes on to say, "Restorative justice is about 'sawubona' (a South African greeting that connotes truly, deeply seeing one another). It is about intentionally cultivating compassion for others, compassion for yourself—we sit in a circle, trying to really see people, to have unconditional positive regard for each other." As a result, restorative justice gives people a chance to right their wrongs, instead of ostracizing or shaming them. If this sounds like the repair of attachment theory, it is. I believe that restorative justice provides us with a deep understanding of how to create secure attachments as well as how to repair them when disrupted.

Teaching empathy to administrators, teachers, and students helps foster secure attachment in that it promotes deep mutual understanding and trust. "This is not a tool in one's toolkit that you pull out situationally," says Bankhead, "it's most effective in environments in which the *whole school* engages in restorative practices." She makes clear that educating a school in restorative practice can take a couple of years because it isn't simply a program, it is a system. Educational restorative justice has spread to the Los Angeles School District and several other districts throughout the nation, but it is by no means the go-to approach for the majority of our youth in the US.

What could our country look like if every school adopted a restorative justice program? As Ron Classen, one of Oakland's pioneers in restorative justice, said, "When you have a punitive system, the automatic response is to deny responsibility because you know you'll get punished. With a restorative justice system in place, the incentive is to admit what you did because you know there is going to be a restorative process to make things right." In other words, if students who violate rules feel acknowledged, related to, and understood in terms of what fueled the behavior, they are much more likely to be accountable and make amends without having to be ostracized from their community.

Restorative practices interrupt the "school-to-prison pipeline" in that they keep kids in school instead of expelling them for violating behavior. A fear many school administrators have about restorative justice is that it won't hold a student accountable and that violations will continue to occur or even increase. But when asked about recidivism, Bankhead emphatically stated, "I know that is typical in the punitive system, that people keep cycling, but we don't have that—once someone has gone through the restorative justice process, which is very labor-intensive, we don't have that [recidivism]."

The new Restorative City Initiative in Oakland hopes to infuse these practices on many levels throughout the community. The possibilities and the effects on our relationships with one another are endless. I believe restorative justice is the epitome of how to repair psychological injuries and increase a sense of safety on a broad-based level.

Mindfulness in Government

Tara Brach, a clinical psychologist and internationally known meditation teacher, had the extraordinary opportunity to teach mindfulness to US Congress members and staff and to judges of the DC Superior Court. Congressman Tim Ryan, who wrote the book *A Mindful Nation,* gave a copy to his colleagues in Congress. These are the seeds of repairing attachment on a national level. As you'll read in my next chapter, there are thousands of studies that indicate the benefits of mindfulness, one of which is the powerful tool of compassion. If the government learned to be more mindful and inclusive in decision making, we could really change the world for the better. There would certainly be less conflict and more effective ways of handling it when it occurred.

Perhaps implementing mindfulness training programs in government bodies, much like Amishi Jha, mindfulness researcher out of the University of Miami, has done with the military, could begin to repair a political divisiveness that has threatened our very democracy. Jha's research entails teaching mindfulness to both soldiers facing combat as well as spouses looking to build resilience to stress. The results, thus far, have been nothing less than extraordinary. Jha found that just eight hours of mindfulness training over a four to eight-week period protected participants from declining attention and mood due to stress. What this means is that fewer soldiers are suffering from the stress of combat and are, as a result, less prone to post-traumatic stress disorder. As a result, we have a more efficient military and a potentially lower suicide rate due to decreased stress and therefore, decreased depression.

Repairing the Personal Relationship

And then there is the art of apology and forgiveness. Humans are not perfect. Sometimes we say mean things to one another. Sometimes we treat each other unfairly. Sometimes we scare each other. When you recognize that you acted in a way that may have caused another harm, acknowledging your behavior by honestly apologizing for it can do a world of wonder. Apologizing doesn't mean that the one harmed quickly responds with forgiveness. She may need to air her hurt feelings. She may feel skeptical of your apology. That's okay. What matters here is that you are accountable when you've hurt someone, intentionally or unintentionally. This acknowledgment *to the other person*, not just to yourself, is the beginning of how to repair a disrupted or injured attachment.

Forgiveness is also a powerful means to repair. It can be harder than an apology, depending on the harm done. It isn't for the faint of heart. Just remember, forgiveness isn't condoning. Instead, it honors the fact that humans aren't perfect, that we make mistakes. Ultimately, forgiveness frees you (the harmed) from the heavy burden of revenge and allows you to move on from the injury.

3

GETTING OUR MINDS AROUND MINDFULNESS
(DON'T SKIP THIS CHAPTER)

"We cannot solve our problems with the same level of thinking that created them."
—Albert Einstein

mind·ful·ness *(noun):* awareness that arises through paying attention, on purpose, in the present moment, nonjudgmentally.

To many people in the United States, practicing mindfulness can feel about as familiar as eating rice with our hands. While people in India or Ethiopia have always eaten food without utensils and people in Viet Nam or Thailand don't look twice at someone meditating on a cushion, we in the US still find it weird to do either. Many Americans assume meditation is for Buddhists or Hindus. Other Americans scoff at the idea of taking time out of their day to sit and, god forbid, do nothing! How on earth can that be helpful when there is so much to do? And still others maintain they are incapable of mindfulness, assuming it means emptying one's mind, which it doesn't.

We race through our days, held hostage by to-do lists, but even when we cross things off, we don't feel satisfied for long. More gets added to the list, and we find ourselves governed by a system that leaves us perpetually stressed. We can't imagine adding "meditate" to this list. That seems like a "waste of time." "I could never sit still for that long," one client says. "I can't clear my mind," another maintains. But what if practicing mindfulness wasn't about clearing your mind or sitting still for long periods of time? Let me tell you a story.

Henry sat across from me, frowning.

"Let it go," he sarcastically stated. "I guess that's the new thing, let it go. Let it go. Let it go!"

I calmly looked at him, taking in his frustration.

"How the hell am I supposed to 'let it go' when my back is throbbing, and my leg is numb? I've done everything—pain meds, physical therapy, acupuncture, stretching, icing…and mindfulness? *Mindfulness?* That Jack Kornfield guy's voice is in my brain. I listen to him all the time and I'm still in pain," he said defiantly.

As a psychologist and Henry's therapist, I had analyzed his chronic pain in the context of his psychological history. Henry had been in chronic emotional pain since I met him some five years earlier. At the time, I had diagnosed him with recurrent major depression in addition to two other diagnoses that don't have relevance to this story. While his depression had become less severe, his latest ailment (the back pain) had become an obsession. Henry's back pain mirrored his emotional pain, and it consumed him, just as his life struggles and negative self-image had consumed him in years prior.

Henry had understandable difficulty seeing the positive in life. His mother had been verbally abusive and abandoned the family when Henry was five. His father was quite self-absorbed and depressed during Henry's childhood and eventually committed suicide, leaving Henry with no family ties. Henry had lived his life feeling unloved and ineffective. He longed for a life partner, but with his biting defenses, it was difficult for him to hang on to a girlfriend for long. He'd already gone through two wives. When he did manage to sustain a relationship, it was often with someone who was equally unavailable as his parents had been. In addition, Henry was in dire straits financially, as his job depended on the use of his back. Suffice it to say, Henry was suffering from a broken heart and now a broken back. He could think of nothing else but his pain. It had become his identity, and cynicism was his cloak.

Beneath the cynicism, however, there was an open place inside him (which was why Jack Kornfield, psychologist and meditation teacher, was in his head.) I had led Henry in some mindfulness meditations during our sessions. This wasn't easy, as Henry was one of the most cynical people I'd ever met, and meditation, to him, felt like a silly, "woo-woo" response to a significant problem. Nonetheless, I had Henry sit squarely, close his eyes, and keep his attention focused on his breath, detailing in his mind the sensations of each inhale and exhale. When his mind became distracted by sound, thought, or emotion, I directed him to simply notice the distraction and nonjudgmentally bring his attention back to his breathing. Sometimes, I guided Henry in progressive relaxation, helping him breathe into tense muscles and use his mind to soften them. I suggested Henry continue these exercises at home with some of Jack's guided meditations. After all, he had developed a little bit of self-compassion and patience over the years and seemed to have the basic tools to follow through with this direction.

Clients come to therapy to talk. They typically don't want to sit in session and "do nothing," as it so appears when one is meditating. My clients are a slice of urban American culture—the overworked, overscheduled, overwhelmed existence that leads people to the doctor's office, the therapy room, and, if they're lucky, the meditation cushion. I say "lucky" because after pouring through gobs of meditation research, spending endless hours meditating myself and guiding clients in my practice on how to live more mindfully, I've concluded that mindfulness meditation allows people to live more happily and healthily. (I know Henry doesn't seem to exemplify this yet, but I'll get back to him.) In fact, research shows that meditation decreases inflammation, improves memory, improves attention, improves mood, helps facilitate healthier relationships, and may even increase longevity. *Most of all, mindfulness meditation lowers cortisol—the stress hormone that, in abundance, negatively affects our physical and mental health.* Still, most of us are skeptical and irritated when we're told that mindfulness could help reduce our stress, so let me bust some mindfulness myths for you.

Mindfulness Myth Busters

"Failure is always an option."
—Adam Savage, *Mythbusters*

The origin of the word "mindfulness" comes from the Pali word "sati." Pali is an Indian language in which much of the original Buddhist teachings were written. Sati (or mindfulness) is not to be confused with the ancient and obsolete practice of Sati in India in which a woman throws herself (and thus kills herself) over her husband's funeral pyre as a ritual! Instead, the "sati" I'm talking about means waking up, remembering the present moment or simply, consciousness.

While mindfulness was propagated by Buddhist philosophy, it is not exclusive to it. The Swiss psychiatrist, Carl Jung, regularly spoke of the power of bringing the unconscious to consciousness, thus living more mindfully. And in the United States, which popularized Buddhist teachings centuries later, mindfulness teaching and practice has grown from a one-man show (Jon Kabat-Zinn, microbiologist and meditation teacher, developed a mindfulness program for hospital patients in the 1970s) to a billion-dollar industry.

Richard Davidson, neuropsychologist at the University of Wisconsin–Madison, where he founded the Center for Healthy Minds, and Daniel Goleman, father of emotional intelligence, took a hard look at the abundance of research on mindfulness and the brain. In their book *Altered Traits: Science Reveals How Meditation Changes Your Mind, Brain, and Body,* the authors conclude that there are many positive impacts mindfulness has on our well-being. Many of them I cited above. But, what fascinated me the most about their findings is that mindfulness can create a "lightness of being" that, in turn, governs how we respond to stress. What is "lightness of being," and how can mindfulness bring it about? To answer this question, let's look at what mindfulness is and what mindfulness is not.

- *"I can't do mindfulness—there is no way I can clear my mind."* Mindfulness *is* paying attention. It *is not* emptying one's mind. When Henry was perseverating on how he'd tried everything to relieve his back pain, listing the numerous interventions and attempted remedies that didn't work, he was not paying attention. He was engaged in a stream of consciousness that was taking him away to a place of frustration and agony. Helping Henry pay attention to his body in that moment with loving kindness brought his mind to the sensations in the body that were present without judging them as bad or trying to eradicate them. In addition, when I asked Henry to focus on his breath, I wasn't asking him to empty his mind. I was simply directing his mind to pay attention to his breath.

- *"I don't have time to just sit and do nothing."* Mindfulness *is* meta-awareness; that is, awareness of awareness. It *is not* "doing nothing." Instead of getting lost in thought or letting one's mind wander, mindfulness both helps us direct thought and be aware of thinking itself. This takes some work. You must observe your thoughts and emotions instead of reacting to them. For example, if you notice the feeling of sadness, instead of identifying it by saying to yourself, "I'm so sad," observe it by saying, "there is sadness." When Henry perseverated by thinking and repeatedly stating to me, "This is terrible. I'm in so much pain!" the pain got worse. But observing pain as sensation allowed him to think about it nonjudgmentally, as neither good nor bad. As Sean Fargo, a former Buddhist monk and current mindfulness teacher in the Bay Area, says, "Mindfulness moves experience from the existential to the phenomenological."

- *"I'm not into meditation."* Mindfulness *can be* a type of meditation, but meditation *doesn't* translate as mindfulness. In other words, one can do a mindfulness meditation by focusing on his or her breath moving in and out of the nose, or one can eat mindfully by noticing the texture and flavor of each bite of food. One can walk mindfully or work mindfully by paying attention, on purpose, in the present moment and nonjudgmentally to each task or each step. Therefore, one can lead a mindful existence without ever meditating (although meditation is excellent training in being mindful.)

- *"I'm not a Buddhist, nor do I believe in any god."* Mindfulness *is* a practice. It *is not* a religion. Although paying attention nonjudgmentally came out of Buddhist philosophy and is practiced regularly in Buddhist and Hindu meditation, it is not a religion. Mindfulness is a way of being in life. It is an approach, a practice, much like exercise or eating healthy are practices. You don't have to sit cross-legged on the floor, chanting mantras to practice mindfulness. Pay attention to the present moment and release judgment. When your mind wanders from the present moment, bring your attention back to the present moment. In doing so, you are practicing mindfulness.

Mindfulness to Cure an Insecure Attachment

"The regular exercise of mindful awareness seems to promote the same benefits that research has found to be associated with childhood histories of secure attachment."

—David Wallin, PhD

In addition to Davidson and Goleman's comprehensive review of mindfulness research, there is David Wallin, attachment theorist, psychologist, and clinician. Wallin has dedicated his career to understanding how psychotherapy can help heal attachment disorders and has incorporated the practice of mindfulness as an essential tool for this healing. In his book *Attachment in Psychotherapy*, published in 2007, Wallin states: "The regular exercise of mindful awareness seems to promote the same benefits—bodily and affective self-regulation, attuned communication with others, insight, empathy, and the like—that research has found to be associated with childhood histories of secure attachment." Furthermore, he makes the case that mindfulness practice, with its focus on nonjudgmental, compassionate awareness, can help create the kind of secure base that humans need to thrive, the kind of base that those who experienced secure attachments in infancy and early childhood have.

55

What does this mean for you? Well, if you have an insecure attachment style, you may want to practice mindfulness as a way to facilitate secure attachments to yourself and others.

"Secure attachment relationships in childhood and psychotherapy help develop this reassuring internal presence by providing us with experiences of being recognized, understood, and cared for that can subsequently be internalized. Mindfulness practice can potentially develop a comparably reassuring internal presence by offering us (glimpsed or sustained) experiences of the selfless, or universal self that is simply awareness. Such experiences are often marked by profound feelings of security, acceptance, and connection, in relation as much to others as to ourselves."[43]

Take, for example, a client of mine I had in group therapy many years ago. I'll call him Larry. Larry was severely depressed and anxious, yearning for social contact but paralyzed by the fear of it. Having never been in psychotherapy before, Larry had his first experience of a safe, nonjudgmental space in which he could reveal his internal world. This world included a harsh negative aspect of himself that repeatedly criticized himself. Larry lived in an internal torture chamber as he ridiculed and berated himself daily for what he said or didn't say, what he did or didn't do. While the group therapy relationships were key in helping Larry establish trust and develop a healthier attachment relationship, teaching him mindfulness meditation that he practiced outside the group proved to be transformative. By mindfully observing his thoughts with *meta-awareness* (that is, being aware of being aware), Larry became less strangled by his self-deprecation and eventually began to create an internal relationship with himself that was less judgmental. As a result, he also projected less judgment onto others. In other words, he became less fearful of appearing like he was "a loser" and more in tune with his present moment surroundings, without judgment.

To think that mindfulness has the power to help heal insecure attachment has far-reaching ramifications. Psychologists have long felt that creating secure attachments in insecurely attached patients was solely dependent on the therapeutic relationship, creating a "corrective emotional experience." In other words, when the therapist is consistently successful in creating a safe, trustworthy space in which he can attune to the patient's verbally reported and nonverbally expressed experience, the patient can begin to feel nonjudgmentally understood and known and can form a more secure sense of self. But if, like Larry, a patient can practice mindfulness outside the therapeutic relationship and further the process of well-being (otherwise indicative of secure attachment), this is an additional useful tool.

Remember why secure attachment is so important? First, it reduces the risk of a host of psychological problems such as anxiety, depression, narcissism, and general defensiveness, to name a few. Second, if you are more secure with herself, you are less stressed. If the symptoms that perpetuate stress are reduced or eradicated, you have a better chance of forming healthy relationships, feeling happier, and thus, making better decisions in life, which leads me to our next topic.

Decisions, Decisions and Evoking Motion (aka emotion)

"You can't make decisions based on fear and the possibility of what might happen."
—Michelle Obama

You may have heard the sayings, "run while you can" or "he's a bat out of hell." These common idioms illustrate the tendency we have as humans to react quickly when we sense danger. The amygdala is the region of the brain that houses our emotional stress responses, such as the flight, fight, freeze response when we feel we're in harm's way (see Chapter One). It can be an extremely useful system when we need to exit a burning building or evade a wild animal. But when we are under *chronic* stress, the amygdala can be reactive and compromise our better judgment or what psychologists call our "executive functions" (the ability to focus attention, learn, manage time, make decisions, and regulate emotion). The executive functions are located in the prefrontal cortex—that is, in the brain's frontal lobe, on the other side of the forehead.

Because the prefrontal cortex that houses executive functions is connected to the amygdala through something called the *default mode network,* when the amygdala is active, it can hijack the prefrontal cortex, causing us to act impulsively—without thinking, so to speak. In other words, the amygdala and prefrontal cortex do not work in balance when someone is chronically stressed. Instead, the amygdala (the emotional center) takes over and can cause a person to forget lines to a song (like Barbara Streisand did at her Central Park performance) or fly into a rage.

Here's the important part: *when we meditate, we activate the prefrontal cortex, which not only focuses our attention but, in turn, quiets the default mode network, thus regulating the amygdala.* As a result, we are less likely to storm out of a frustrating meeting at work and more likely to offer feedback calmly if we disagree with something.

This is true not just for seasoned meditators, but for beginners, too. One study showed that non-meditators who took an eight-week MBSR course did better on cognitive tasks that tested these executive functions than before they took the course.[44] Furthermore, Davidson and Goleman report that just ten minutes of mindfulness seems to temporarily improve concentration, eight minutes of mindfulness temporarily lessens mind-wandering, and about ten hours of mindfulness over a two-week period strengthens attention and working memory, which, in one study, led to improved scores on a graduate school entrance exam among trained participants. (Stressed-out students have much to gain from practicing mindfulness, which might be why the popular mindfulness app Calm added a Mindfulness 101 for college students and more colleges and universities are adding meditation rooms to their campuses.)

The key to sustaining improved attention, concentration, and working memory is to sustain one's mindfulness practice. Short-term meditation and mindfulness training render short-term results. Altered traits (or permanent changes) occur with sustained practice over the course of years. Therefore, if you want to be a less reactive person and a more focused decision-maker when it comes to day-to-day life, you'll need to bank some substantial hours of mindfulness practice.

I return to Henry. He was fifty-seven when he underwent back surgery for a herniated disc that had been causing him increasing and unbearable pain for the past two years. Immediately after the surgery, he experienced relief. He could almost stand up straight, walk without wincing, and he could sleep! However, daily doses of oxycodone may have masked the fact that nothing in his back had actually changed since the surgery.

The problem became apparent merely sixteen weeks later when, medication-free, the pain became unbearable again. Henry sought a second opinion from another surgeon who indicated that Henry was possibly a victim of "failed back surgery" (a 20–40 percent chance of occurrence, according to a 2016 article in the *Journal of Pain Research*).

It had taken Henry two years and numerous discussions in psychotherapy to muster the courage to have the surgery in the first place, so when the pain returned, it was intensely discouraging. After being batted from one pain clinic to another, from one doctor to another, one day in my office, Henry broke down into unrelenting tears, his back against the couch, his head in his hands, hopeless that he'd ever be pain-free again. That day, I sat with Henry's grief and asked him to bring mindful awareness to his emotions as they manifested as sensations in the body. Henry followed my guidance, and I was relieved to see that he left the office calmer.

I decided to keep up with the mindfulness exercises as we simultaneously addressed his mixed fear of and desire for another surgery. Calming Henry's nervous system allowed him to sleep better, and his increased sleep efficiency seemed to improve his cognitive abilities. In turn, this allowed for better concentration and focus when making decisions, including the decision to have another surgery, this time with a different surgeon.

The results were astounding. Two weeks after the second surgery, Henry waltzed—yes, waltzed—into my office with an upright posture and a smile on his face. "I think it worked!" he exclaimed. He was taking no medication and was pain-free. This state persisted, week after week. He was sleeping eight hours a night. He was meditating daily. He felt happy and hopeful. The transformation was truly remarkable.

While I do not believe that I was the sole reason Henry so mindfully tuned in to what he needed and had a successful medical procedure, nor do I know whether the actual procedure was the only cure to Henry's pain, I am aware that guiding him in mindfulness practice, despite worsening physical symptoms helped. Henry accepted my guidance, practiced mindfulness, and gained a stronger sense of self with a more objective mind.

It was Henry's stronger self that carefully researched his options, tuned into his various emotions without identifying with them, and made a sound decision about his circumstance. Dan Goleman and

Richard Davidson would say that Henry got "unstuck" from his distressing emotions by meditating on them. As a result, Henry had cultivated the tools to experience pain differently. After the second surgery, when he experienced occasional twinges, he no longer reacted to them, and, therefore, didn't get stuck in the pain. Remember that meditation strengthens executive functions, which, in turn, makes for more thoughtful decision making. In other words, as Henry's emotions stopped driving his behavior, he was able to look at his pain and his dilemma with less judgment and more objectivity. As a result, his "woe is me, nothing will help me" belief began to wane, and his mood improved.

Not only does mindfulness meditation protect you from getting caught up in yourself and from making knee-jerk reactions to stressors, it helps you tune into your emotions with nonjudgment and compassion. It helps you become aware of what you are feeling, so you can better regulate your emotions instead of letting your emotions regulate you. This is extremely beneficial for people struggling with anxiety and depression, or for people just having a bad day. When depressed or running in circles with anxiety, the internal "I" and "me" statements tend to be negative and repetitive. For example, "I'm a failure, I'm too fat, I'll never be successful" can be an ongoing internal monologue that oppresses your spirit and depresses your motivation, hope, and energy, leading to depression or heightening anxiety. My client, Larry, experienced this negative self-absorption in spades, but as he worked in therapy while simultaneously becoming more mindful, the internal negative self-talk became less intense.

The realization that emotions are temporary and don't have to define you allows you to refocus your attention on the task at hand and see the silver linings in otherwise difficult circumstances. In other words, you can note "there is sadness," but you can also note "there is beauty" beneath the sadness. By doing this, you activate potential instead of squelching it, which decreases stress.

There are so many aspects of mindfulness that can provide relief from stress that I'm going to refer to additional mindfulness concepts and exercises in subsequent chapters. For now, let's get to a hot topic these days—anxiety—and look at how to apply mindfulness (and other interventions) to it.

4

ANXIOUS AMERICANS:
WHY WE LIVE IN A WORRIED WORLD

"Anxiety is like a rocking chair. It gives you something to do but doesn't get you very far."

—Jodi Picoult, author

anx-i-e-ty *(noun)*: a feeling of worry, nervousness, or unease, typically about an imminent event or something with an uncertain outcome.

Why is it that anxiety has become the number one psychological disorder in the United States since the turn of the millennium? It's not just teens suffering from skyrocketing numbers of social anxiety, nor your average, overworked, corporate employee who make up the 31 percent of Americans who qualify for an anxiety disorder at some point in life. It can be any and every one of us residing in the US. Are we really just feeling more alienated from each other than ever before? Is that why my son loved that small-town feeling of the fictional Mayberry in which the characters supported vs. feared each other? I believe detachment from each other is a common thread in the three subsections of anxiety I've outlined below: *Generalized Anxiety, Social Anxiety,* and *Death Anxiety.* But it isn't the only thread. Our anxiety is intertwined with numerous stressors we don't even realize are there.

Generalized Anxiety (The Tendency to Worry about Something Every Day)

His heart had been racing for weeks. He had trouble sleeping at night. He wondered if he was developing a heart condition, as he'd never felt his heart pound like this. His worry was specific but vague. He worried about his sons—one unemployed and in a bad relationship, the other drinking too much. His wife was worried, too, but instead of supporting her husband, she took it out on him—he'd been too lax, hadn't been an involved enough father, so "no wonder they're in trouble," she maintained.

He didn't know exactly what could happen but often feared that one or both of his now-adult children could die. He also worried about what they were doing at night, whom they were with and where they were hanging out. He sometimes texted and called them incessantly, and when he got no response, he paced the house and worried more, unconsciously looking for soothing. He felt helpless to do anything about their less-than-optimal situations, as they were both out of the house now, and he had no jurisdiction over them. Instead, he tried deep breathing, meditating, biking at the gym, and telling himself things could be worse—that, in the grand scheme of life, everything would be okay. But nothing he did or said affected the consistent, rapid heartbeat. It continued to pound at an erratic and relentlessly uncommon pace, making his already-worried mind become even more worried. He went to the medical doctor. He was prescribed a heart monitor, which he wore for a week. The test result rendered the following diagnosis: generalized anxiety disorder.

This is the story of my friend, Michael. After he received the anxiety diagnosis, he was sent for a psychiatric medication evaluation and eventually put on Lexapro (a selective serotonin reuptake inhibitor used to treat depression and anxiety) along with Klonopin (an anti-anxiety medication often used for more immediate relief of anxiety symptoms). The fears about his sons, coupled with lack of spousal support and economic strain, had gone beyond an acute or chronic stress response and had morphed into a constant state of feeling out of control.

Sometimes, it's hard to tell the difference between stress and anxiety. Both are often accompanied by physical symptoms. And sometimes, what starts as a stress response turns into anxiety. For example, when Michael learned his eighteen-year-old son was caught driving under the influence and put in jail, he jumped out of his chair, grabbed the car keys, and drove to the jail. His body was thrust into a fight, flight, freeze response. As he drove, his heart pounded and his hands became sweaty, as he was suffering from acute stress. Then, after two more alcohol-related incidences, when it became clear Michael's son had a drinking problem, this added to his underlying anxiety, putting Michael into a constant state of worry. This worry generalized to his other son, his marriage, and even his job. He imagined everything in his life was going to hell in a handbasket.

Michael's story exemplifies what I mean by generalized anxiety, in that his worries may have begun with one thing but generalized to several others that were or weren't happening in his life. He would often lie awake at night, feeling his pounding heart as his mind darted from the fear of confronting a subordinate at work to the fear of his ailing parents dying to the fear his sons were on a bad track in life. Anxiety can be contagious in this way. In a domino effect, it can begin with a particular problem and extend to many.

One of the most common anxiety complaints these days is the fear of running out of time. Deepak Chopra once said that the more we fear running out of time, the more we are doing just that—running out of the present. Anxiety likes to fester in the unknown, imaginary future. It breeds on all that *could* go wrong. This is why when I ask my anxious clients what they are worried about, they often have a hard time answering. They jump from one thing to another, overwhelming themselves with perceived yet unrealized threats. They know they are anxious because they feel it in their bodies or find they can't concentrate, are snappy, or just exhausted.

The medications initially helped Michael, but he was wise enough to know they weren't the entire solution to his problem. He got himself into therapy, eventually weaned off the meds, and began a daily meditation practice. He worked hard to stay in the moment. For example, instead of being defensive with his typically accusatory wife, he empathized with her. These interventions helped calm Michael's nervous system and brought him closer to his wife, which increased the health of their attachment. This attachment, strengthened via empathy, gave Michael more resilience to stress. Strength in numbers isn't just a saying. When we're more intimately connected to others, we are more resilient to stress.

Hacks for Generalized Anxiety (Aka Everyday Worry)
The Science of Slowing Our Breathing: When we slow our breathing, we activate the vagus nerve, which links the brain, heart, gut, and lungs. Because the vagus nerve is part of the parasympathetic nervous system (the calming part of the nervous system), it serves to calm almost all areas of the body. If the body is calmer, the mind is also calmer, and vice versa. Because our bodies and minds are intertwined, anxiety can increase in response to a physical symptom. For example, when Michael became aware of his

pounding heart, he became more anxious. He perceived the physical sensation as another bad sign or threat. If we can tame the physical sensations in our bodies by bringing nonjudgmental, compassionate awareness to the body experience, we can derail the merry-go-round of anxiety.

The Exercise: *Wherever you are right now, sitting, standing, or lying down, straighten your spine to evoke an awake position. Bring your attention to your breath, noticing its reliable rhythm as it moves in and out of your body. Just notice the breath as it manifests in the rise and fall of your chest, the expansion or contraction of the abdomen, or via the sensation of the air as it passes through your nostrils. Now, begin to elongate the breaths, counting slowly to six as you inhale and counting slowly to six as you exhale. Do this five or six times. Now, take notice of what area of your body is particularly tense or unsettled. This may be your pounding heart, your nervous stomach, your tight chest, neck, or head. Gently and compassionately place your hand or hands on that area of the body and continue the breathing, imagining sending the soothing breath to this area of the body.*

The Science of Focusing Our Attention: Remember the default mode network from Chapter Three? It generally defines the region of the brain that is active when one is not engaged in focused activity. It's the part of the brain that, given downtime, tends to think, worry, or ruminate, usually about oneself. While contemplation and planning are useful, worry is not. With worry, we wind up on a merry-go-round we can't get off of because we refuse to disembark until we find the solution to the problem that hasn't yet occurred. It's crazy-making, to say the least. Often, people who are anxious and are "at rest" inadvertently engage the worried mind because they are not engaged in an activity.

The Exercise: Limit your worry time. You may remember the *Reader's Digest* quote by Mark Twain: *"I am an old man and have known a* *great many troubles, but most of them never happened."* We worry because we believe that if we think about all that could happen, we'll figure out how to magically prevent it. Begin to notice how much time you spend worrying about things you can't control or that haven't happened. If you find yourself sitting on the couch, lost in the story of "me," set a timer for ten minutes and, when the timer goes off, if you are still worrying, get up and engage in an activity that requires focus—like cooking, bike riding, sewing, or paying bills. Not only will the activity engage your prefrontal cortex and quiet the default mode network that plays reruns of all the terrible things that could happen, but it will instill in you the art of being present.

Why allow yourself even ten minutes? Because it's important to acknowledge your thoughts, and because you can't be engaged in something all the time. But, if you allow your thoughts to run amok, by the time you "wake up," you may have wound yourself into a stressed mess, and it will be harder to get out. It's more realistic to shorten your worry time than expect yourself not to worry at all. The more you shorten your time worrying, the more your brain will get used to the non-worried state, and your sympathetic nervous system will appreciate that. You'll feel less anxious less often. We can choose where to rest our minds, even if that means we have to redirect them multiple times a day.

Social Anxiety (The Tendency to Worry Regularly about What Others Are Thinking)

The rate of social anxiety in the United States is high. Joyable, an online mental health service, indicates that 70 percent of our millennials are anxious, with social anxiety being a common complaint. And what do millennials do when they are socially anxious? Bury themselves in social media and smartphones, which apparently increases social anxiety! Jean Twenge, PhD attributes this startling statistic to an increase in social comparison and extrinsic values. Her research shows that youth today have far more opportunity than youth of previous generations to compare their lives with the lives of others, given the pervasive use of social media.[45] Sites like Facebook, Snapchat, and Instagram tend to encourage a "look at me!" mentality. As tweens and teens post pictures of themselves and their lives on these sites, they not only track them to see how many "likes" they get, but they stalk the sites of friends, acquaintances, and celebrities, comparing themselves to other people's personas.

I say *personas* because that is what social media sites lure people to do—create personas. A persona is like a role or a character one adopts in order to present what she thinks is a positive, likable image of herself to the world. Think of it as a mask that conveys a simple, captivating face while hiding the more complex, true one. The mask becomes the image our youth are then pressured to uphold, more so than previous generations who didn't have such a venue for persona displays. Forty-five percent of Z gens feel judged on social media, which may be why they create the persona in the first place.

Furthermore, Twenge's research points to a generational increase in extrinsic goals, such as fame and wealth. Such aims may seem tantalizing in that they connote power and, therefore, the possibility of more "likes." But in reality, they are merely shiny objects that, when attained, wind up being short-lived Band-Aids to contentment. Research has always shown that relationships with one another (I mean the real ones, not the digital ones) are what make us happy. Yet, teens and millennials seem to be chasing the money/fame dragon, which only results in more stress, as very few people attain either. If they happen to attain their extrinsic goals, these same fame-chasers don't actually feel any better about themselves.

Nevertheless, teens suffer from extrinsically-motivated and persona-based lifestyles, both of which can feel like trying to hold grains of sand in your fist. Their lives are tenuously maintained only by the stress of tightening control over what people see and don't see about them. Like the grains of sand, their image can easily slip away from them, resulting in a vigilant and stressful stance in life. The focus of what others think of them far exceeds the normal adolescent dilemma of wanting approval from peers. It has moved onto a world stage that has the potential to backfire into extreme isolation and social anxiety for many.

Adults are prone to social anxiety, too, though. Do you have the experience of calling someone on the phone and hoping it goes to voicemail so you don't have to interact live? That's a little bit of social anxiety. Do you whip out your phone as soon as you step into a quiet elevator of people? A touch of social anxiety. Do you avoid eye contact in the grocery store with someone you know but don't feel like talking to? Could be social anxiety. Now, I certainly don't expect everyone to be gregarious and talkative. That would be unreasonable and undesirable. Introverts are a huge asset to our society, and, as Susan Cain illustrates in her book, *Quiet: The Power of Introverts in a World That Can't Stop Talking,* introverts are greatly misunderstood. I am, however, talking about the importance of basic human connection—how to foster it without overwhelming yourself. Read below to understand how to overcome social anxiety without having to be a social butterfly.

Solutions to SAD (Social Anxiety Disorder, Not Seasonal Affective Disorder!)

For Individuals:

Practice Compassion (Both for Yourself and Others). Mother Teresa knew decades ago that compassion was healing. Since she set foot in India, offering her compassionate services to the hungry and vulnerable, a plethora of research has immerged on the power compassion has on our well-being, including reducing anxiety. The concept is simple, really. If we have compassion for ourselves and others, we free ourselves from the scary burden of judgment (you know, that fear of looking like a fool). Compassion is not selfish. Compassion is not pity. Compassion is understanding oneself or another without criticism.

Kristin Neff, psychologist and compassion researcher, says: "Self-compassion makes us more willing to accept, experience and acknowledge difficult feelings with kindness—which paradoxically helps us process and let go of them more fully." Think about it—if you are kind to yourself, others' criticisms don't penetrate you as much because you are already sturdy in the acceptance of yourself. How do you practice self-compassion? Start by simply saying to yourself, "I see you, I accept you, and I'm here for you." You can be kindly curious about mistakes you make, but not critical of them. Self-compassion does not mean you let yourself run amok, dismissing wrongdoings. It means you love yourself despite your wrongdoings; it means you can look at all of who you are because you're not killing yourself with demoralizing criticisms.

Deep Breathing. This is an invaluable exercise for social anxiety. Before you go into a social situation, practice the breathing exercise I gave you in the section "Hacks for Generalized Anxiety." Start prior to arriving at school, or a social or work-related event. Then, continue to practice the slow breathing as you walk into the venue, counting to five with every inhale and again to five with every exhale. You can combine the breathing with the self-compassionate statement: "I see you, I accept you, and I'm here for you." You can continue the breathing exercise (without the counting) even while in conversation. Remember that breathing slowly and deeply calms the nervous system, and, while it may not entirely cure your anxiety, it can serve to take the edge off of it, which will help integrate you more comfortably into the social situation.

Desensitize. One of the more traditional ways to treat phobias is to help people get increasingly close and familiar with the thing they are afraid of. If, for example, someone is afraid of driving across bridges, we start with a mindfulness exercise that entails imagining looking at a bridge, then imagining approaching the bridge, then imagining being on the bridge. All the while, the patient breathes deeply. Then, we move into the real world of looking at the real bridge, slowly approaching it, and actually driving across the bridge. This process can take weeks or months, but it is often effective. It's called *desensitization*. You can do something similar with social anxiety. If you are afraid of speaking in class, for example, you can start by asking a student or a teacher a question after class. You can slowly add to that by raising your hand in class to ask another question. You can then add to that by eventually offering your opinion on a subject in front of the class. *All of this is done slowly and with self-compassion, not criticism!*

For Schools:

Weekly Tech-Free Days. Did you know that 30 percent of our schools require kids to use tablets or laptops for class and homework? Did you know that approximately the same percentage of teens are anxious? Because kids often try to soothe their anxiety by burying themselves in their devices, and because we, as adults, didn't protect them from the addictive nature of devices, we owe them a little help. One idea is for schools to implement tech-free days once a week, in which tablets and laptops are to be left at home and phones checked only before or after school. On a tech-free day, teaching can be done via group discussion, pencil and paper writing, and mindfulness practice. Just one day may be a drop in the bucket, but it is a place to start. It could interrupt the vicious cycle of using screens to respond to social anxiety and show students that working with each other or contemplatively by themselves can feel rewarding, not scary.

Mindfulness in Schools. Teaching mindfulness in schools is slowly becoming more prevalent but has a long way to go. After all, many districts don't have money to afford mindfulness instructors or to train their staff. Programs like Oakland's Mindful Schools or movie director, David Lynch's, Quiet Time program that brings transcendental meditation into Los Angeles schools, have made a significant impact. The University of California, Davis conducted a large randomized-controlled study on Mindful Schools' effectiveness with Oakland's elementary school children. Researchers concluded that Mindful Schools' six-week mindfulness program improved student focus, class participation, emotion regulation, and compassion for others. Another study indicated that a Mindful Schools curriculum reduced depression in minority children. David Lynch's program proved to increase student alertness, increase resilience to stress, decrease students' blood pressure, and decrease anger, tension, depression, and anxiety among undergraduate and graduate students attending several East Coast universities. These are model programs for other groups or cities looking to implement mindfulness practice into their schools.

I recommend that mindfulness instructors in training consider doing their mindfulness teaching requirement in schools. In many ways, we have neglected our youth by giving them devices that are as addictive as crack and then expecting them to maintain a sense of self and intimacy with others, despite the fact that the devices can decrease attention and raise anxiety. If we actually attended to our kids by teaching them the power of mindful connection to their bodies, thoughts, and feelings, instead of allowing them to perpetuate the art of tuning out, we could likely make a dent in the epidemic of social anxiety.

Restorative Justice. I already put a plug in for the power and importance of implementing educational restorative justice in all our schools, but I will now explain how it might have an impact on social anxiety. Social anxiety is driven by the fear of judgment. Traditional disciplinary systems are punitive—they center on the concept of judgment. If we change our approach from a punitive to an inclusive one, while still holding kids that violate rules accountable, in a restorative way, students will have less to fear from their schools and their peers. They may be less defensive, less anxious, and, as the research indicates, there will be fewer violations.

In addition, the students themselves interact in community-building groups in which they learn to tell their story, listen to one another, and deeply see the other person. They also participate in harm circle groups, where they come together and discuss boundary-crossing behavior and how to repair and heal harm that one person may have caused another. Won't they fear each other less if they start to know each other more? No one is better than anyone else. If they are taught to understand the root of behavior, they are also being taught what Kristen Neff refers to as "an understanding of our common humanity." When there is understanding and acceptance, it's much harder to feel afraid. To this date no research has been conducted on whether educational restorative justice can reduce social anxiety, but given the fact that it's philosophy is about community-building, repair and healing, all of which have been associated with reducing anxiety, I believe it is one of our biggest hopes for the future.

Death Anxiety

"It was 2016… and it was as if the world had turned upside down. It was full of darkness."

—Brittany Howard, singer/songwriter

In 2014, one of my clients, Peter, would tell me he lay awake nightly, worrying about terrorism in our city of Seattle. Just a few months prior, two men were shot and killed outside a nightclub, and not long before that, a man had been shot and killed walking home from the store. Both incidents were traced to the same man, Ali Muhammed Brown, whose motives were terroristic in nature but not deemed federal offenses based on the vagueness of Brown's affiliations.

Peter couldn't get his mind off the possibility that he, his wife, his twelve-year-old son or ten-year-old daughter could be ambushed on any given day on any street in Seattle. Already struggling with stout anxiety, Peter developed obsessive-compulsive disorder. He regularly and repeatedly checked the doors of his home to make sure they were locked. He struggled nightly to fall asleep and woke up to the slightest noise, which he routinely responded to by rechecking doors and windows. He ruminated daily about airport terrorism (a sign of 9/11's effect) and seceded from flying for two entire years.

I worked extensively with Peter on building a stronger sense of self through internal compassion, support, and encouragement. Peter's upbringing had been lonely. A critical mother left him feeling he could do no right, and an absent father left him feeling unimportant and un-soothed. He anxiously needed reassurance and consoling yet avoided closeness with others.

While these circumstances and psychological constructs laid the groundwork for decades of depression and anxiety, Peter's obsessive-compulsive symptoms, triggered by the Seattle shootings, appeared as an overlay to his baseline anxiety.

I employed mindfulness exercises and guided him during the meditations to help calm his nervous system and reduce preoccupation. I taught him desensitization techniques in order to habituate the environments that left him hypervigilant. I helped him limit his worry time (see below) and have hope (also below). The interventions helped, and Peter's OCD waned. But, as United States politics ramped up, culminating in the divisive and scandalous 2016 election, Peter returned to a minimally consolable state. So, we began re-applying the interventions to Peter's newest anxieties.

Peter's case is a classic example of how our country's climate can psychologically affect us. While Peter was already an anxious person, it is noteworthy that the external tragedies of rising terrorism and racial hatred threw him over the proverbial edge. Let's look at current phenomena that are increasing death anxiety in our country: mass shootings, climate change, and terrorism.

Mass Shootings

Whether gun violence is becoming more prevalent or just more publicized is often up for debate. While it matters for legal purposes, it doesn't as much for psychological purposes. That's because our general awareness of, and more recent exposure to, myriad mass shootings have left Americans rattled and scared. It's one thing to know you live in a crime-ridden neighborhood where gang-related shootings are a common occurrence. While stressful, you learn where to and where not to go and with whom to associate (or not associate). But, with America's mass shootings, they happen randomly and seemingly anywhere, leaving all of us at the mercy of it happening to us, to our children.

Take, for example, the recent incident at an upscale yoga studio in Florida. Did any of these mindful yoga-goers imagine that their studio, tucked above a lovely Italian restaurant, would be the scene of a mass murder? No. Did the concert-goers at the country music festival in Las Vegas imagine that fifty-eight of them would be killed and another 851 injured that evening as a result of 1,100 rounds of fire from an armed madman hiding out on the thirty-second floor of the Mandalay Bay Hotel? No. Did some of these survivors imagine it could actually happen again, a year later, at a bar in Thousand Oaks, California? No. Or, did my friend, Judy, think she'd end up hiding out in the back of a convenience store with her husband, ten-year-old daughter, store manager, and other innocent customers when shooting broke out during a Black Lives Matter march in Dallas? She and her family had been in town for a sports tournament for her older son who was innocently back at their hotel while Judy, her husband and daughter spent two hours in a living hell only to have to escape out a back door, jump a fence and run for their lives.

Apparently, anyone can be shot anywhere these days. People begin to realize they really can't do much to protect themselves from these sorts of crimes. For those who have an already-vigilant disposition in life, it is terrifying. Domestic terrorism, like the above examples, instills a fluctuating but ever-present anxiety about dying. My client, Peter, is an example of what it is like to suffer from death anxiety in relation to the fear of being shot.

Terrorism

9/11 was the first hit. It happened before my second son was even born. He's never lived without strict airport security or the acceptance that international enemies could terrorize our cities or neighborhoods and annihilate us. It's part of his reality. For those of us who hadn't considered that international terrorism could really happen on US soil, we had to face a shift in our reality. Not only did it happen, but it's happened again and again and poses a constant threat today.

I remember when the government first introduced the color-coded threat levels designed to alert Americans of the risk that a terrorist event could occur. While it may have rallied law enforcement, it only served to freak me out. *We're at an orange? Maybe I shouldn't fly to Oakland to see my friends and family as planned.* The publicized threat levels were always yellow, orange, or red. Why didn't we ever hear about the blue level threat or, god forbid, the green (low-risk) threat? Some speculated the color-coded warnings were a politically manipulative tool designed to boost support for the president. Others simply questioned their validity.

In 2009, the color-coded threat system was essentially removed from the public eye. After all, reports had begun to come out about how it was negatively affecting Americans' mental health. While this may have eased the minds of some Americans, others still live with some background awareness that our country isn't as safe as we thought. I admit that I think twice when attending huge stadium events during politically tense times. I'm also choosy about where I travel.

Recently, my friend, Lane, excitedly signed herself up for a photography venture in the architecturally beautiful country of Iran. As the trip approached, the terrorism threat level for Americans traveling to other countries, found on the travel advisory section of the Homeland Security website, reported a "do not travel" warning for Iran. Lane was torn. She'd looked forward to this trip for a year, had never been to Iran, and had been thrilled to have the opportunity to shoot photos there and get to know the culture. After much contemplation and reassurance from her Iranian guide, she decided to go forward with the travel despite the warning.

Once Lane set foot on Iranian soil, however, she realized she may have made a mistake. Locals warned this lone group of Americans that it was not common to see them there. They said if the American president pulled out of the Iranian nuclear deal, Americans wouldn't be safe on their soil. Lane's biggest fear was being detained. A representative at the US State Department had warned her that while detainment wasn't likely, it would be pretty dire if it happened, insinuating the probability of torture and low likelihood of being rescued. So, while the scenery and photo ops were apparently unparalleled, Lane lived with the constant worry that she could die. She stayed hyper-alert, stayed close to her guide, and followed all rules, as it was clear their travel group was being watched.

One would think that Lane would feel great relief being back in the States after the stressful Iranian trip. But Lane admits that even here in the United States, she worries about a possible terrorist attack. "I definitely check doors and exits when I'm at large events," she states. Sounds a little like Peter. But Lane doesn't have obsessive-compulsive disorder. Her worry about large events is just the way it is here now since 9/11. It's how many of us think.

Climate Change (Where Will We Go?)

Contrary to some beliefs, climate change is really happening. In fact, the most recent climate change report from thirteen federal agencies indicates that we are in for quite a ride. Not only does it predict that the devastating wildfires we recently saw in California will get worse, but it indicates they will spread to other parts of the country, such as the Northeast, a region that rarely grapples with wildfire issues. Most disturbing is the reported hit our economy will take as crops fail and American exports and supply chains suffer. Sound dystopian? It is. And, yet, we are currently run by an administration that is all for environment deregulation, making climate change a more urgent situation.

Whether one thinks about it regularly or not, the thought that our planet is dying lies in the depths of everyone's psyches. The possibility of a lost world is reflected in books and film. Think: *The Hunger Games, Ready Player One,* or *Black Mirror.* In fact, that's almost all there is for our kids to read or watch these days. Could it be that the millennials and the Z gens are just slightly depressed, and that's why they don't form close relationships? Could the feeling that it's all a dying world anyway be contributing to their increasing anxiety and depression?

Some clients bring up climate change in the context of their depressed mood. They relay a feeling of futility, a hopelessness that comes when one can't imagine an abundant future. Others start to talk about it but say it makes them too anxious, so they change the subject. Climate change is the ultimate death. We know we will die individually, but there is comfort in knowing that the world lives on, that our DNA may live on in our children and that our legacies could continue. But if the planet itself is no longer inhabitable, nothing lives on. So where do we go from there?

Dealing with Death Anxiety

Acknowledge Negative Feelings. First, you have to go to the darkness. That's right, you have to allow yourself to feel what you're feeling (even fear or despair) instead of just worrying about it. If you go toward feelings, they have a better chance of passing. If you hang out in Worryland, keeping the sadness or fear at bay, anxiety sets in, and feelings aren't truly acknowledged. Trust me; if feelings aren't truly acknowledged, they will eat away at you somehow—as fatigue, headaches, irritability, and so on. So, what does it mean to acknowledge feelings instead of pushing them away or denying them?

Feel the despair of shooting rampages by saying to yourself, "There is despair." Feel the sadness of climate change by noting, "There is sadness." Allow yourself to cry or to tell someone you're scared or say it out loud to yourself. By acknowledging the feelings as states of mind that come and go, they are less intimidating. This entails awareness. You first have to pause, perhaps allow yourself to sit alone long enough and without distraction in order to make room for the feelings such as the ones I named above. Or, you can talk about them with someone else. In these ways, you acknowledge the presence of difficult feelings and give them the airtime they deserve. If the Parkland students had stayed bottled up, they wouldn't have had the strength—gained from the connection of mourning together—to activate like they did.

Don't worry, I won't leave you here with feelings of despair. You may assume that purposely feeling the negativity sounds engulfing or worse, but without this step we can't move onto the next one. And there is a next one.

Widen the Lens. This step is not about denying what's there, nor is it about positive thinking. It's about seeing more than death and envisioning a realistic picture of how things may go better. In the case of my client's fear that he or one of his children could be shot, I got him to think about the bigger picture: that, while we've been media exposed to many shootings, they are actually rare; that law enforcement is more prevalent at his kids' school these days than it was a year prior; that the majority of people live long lives and, therefore, he and his children are likely to live long lives, too; that his son and daughter are alive and well right now, and he can play with them, laugh with them, eat with them, and so on. They are not dead. Widening the lens helped remind him of the bigger picture.

So, if you fear gun violence, for example, try to remember all the individual states that have enacted legal restrictions on buying guns.

Try to remind yourself we're a country in evolution, a country that could eventually change its laws or improve its mental health system or whatever you feel needs to happen to reduce gun violence. Think bigger picture and imagine a better or alternative outcome to the problem that's presently getting you down.

Last, if you or someone you love is truly dying, this exercise is even more valuable. Clinging to something like life when we're dying only increases stress and tension. Imagine death as one part of the life journey. It doesn't exist on its own. It's transformation from one form to another. A passage. In this way, you widen the lens of death itself instead of limiting it to being bad or frightening.

Activate Hope. Now that you've widened the lens, allow that bigger picture vision to instill hope in you. Hope gets us to move as we believe there is something to go toward. If we feel anxious (as in insecure anxious attachment), we can get stymied in a "we're all going to die!" mentality. If we feel futility (as in avoidant attachment) we can dismiss all that is possible and inadvertently create a self-fulfilling prophecy, as in "we're all going to die anyway, so what's the point?" By activating hope, you pull yourself off insecure responses to death anxiety and push yourself into motivation for solution. Elon Musk says he's motivated by feelings of sadness about the planet dying, even if that means finding a way to live on Mars. In this way, he has hope that we can survive even climate change.

Identify what stresses you out and find organizations addressing that problem, be they organizations that work to save the rain forest, reduce gun violence, eradicate racial profiling. Even giving $10 to an organization that is doing something about your fear can empower you, make you feel less anxious and happier.

5

THE EPIDEMIC OF LONELINESS

"The world is suffering from an epidemic of loneliness. If we cannot rebuild strong, authentic social connections, we will continue to splinter apart."

—Vivek Murthy
Nineteenth Surgeon General of the United States

lone-li-ness *(noun):* 1. sadness because one has no friends or company. 2. isolation

My client, whom I'll call "Nancy," suffers from generalized anxiety and persistent depression. She starts most sessions, sitting silently on the couch while tears stream down her face. "I'm so lonely," she manages to eke out. It's not the first time I've heard those words from Nancy. She's spoken them many times in various affective states—sad, angry, scared, hopeless. In fact, Nancy is one of many clients who feels this way.

Despite living in a metropolitan area of nearly four million people, my clients are struggling to connect. Yes, they are my clients, so perhaps they come to me for help because they have difficulty navigating relationships. But that doesn't explain why 47 percent of the US population views loneliness as a public health problem, and 58 percent of Americans believe loneliness is a result of technology use.[46] Is it?

Nancy is a divorced woman, single mother, sole proprietor, and lives alone (except when her son is with her four days a week). She forces herself to the gym, to an occasional book reading and engages in online-dating, but comes home feeling unknown and unloved. The estrangement is killing her. She lies awake at night worrying about her future, her son, money. When she follows my suggestions to reach out to acquaintances or long-lost friends, to engage in an interest, even if theoretical, to meditate as a way of fostering internal connection and easing social anxiety, it temporarily helps. Often, she gets lured by the TV or Facebook, looking for something, someone. She winds up reading her ex-husband's Facebook posts about his booming business and busy social life, gets jealous, then loses hope.

Dan is also single. He spends most of his time working a job that doesn't fulfill him because, with a chronic illness, he is dependent on the health benefits it offers. He comes home exhausted, and he, too, lies awake at night—anxious and depressed about his future. He does have close friendships and good family relationships but finds little time to nourish them as he tries to make ends meet. He longs for a girlfriend, especially because all his friends are married, but doesn't know how to meet people without being online—a dating system he finds depressing.

Both Dan and Nancy have chronic physical illnesses. They are highly dependent on their health insurance to cover the astronomical costs of medical care they need. Both have anxious attachments to our nation—dependent on it, but afraid it will pull the rug out from under them. They often don't sleep at night, worrying that they will lose their healthcare and then be docked for a preexisting condition if they try to sign on with a new carrier. These two people live a mere half-mile from one another but have never met. Each suffers in his or her respective loneliness, not knowing they share similar circumstances. There are countless stories today like Dan and Nancy's.

Because loneliness is measured by one's *perception* rather than objective time spent with others, many people are lonely despite numerous human interactions a day. In fact, a person can be highly engaged with a team at work, a book club in the evening, and a family to go home to at night and still feel lonely. Certainly, if one is already suffering from depression, he will likely feel lonely, as depression does seem to cause loneliness. But research indicates that loneliness also causes depression, making this relationship bidirectional.

Perhaps the biggest problem of loneliness today is that it causes people to fear other people. Intimidated by what they think others' lives are like, lonely people fear being seen and known, as they believe that they are falling short in some way—they're worried they're not pretty enough, not interesting enough, not smart enough. These fears cause them to retreat further, rendering them more likely to stay home on a Friday night than attempt a meet-up with a group of friends or strangers. They feel thin-skinned. Loneliness hurts, and often lonely people feel they cannot withstand one more rejection. Instinctively, they avoid the "danger" of the outside world and instead choose to be alone. This leaves them in a feedback loop of loneliness, retreat and, therefore, more loneliness. What's worse is that when lonely people try to explain the reason for their loneliness. they usually come up with a litany of perceived flaws or inadequacies which puts them in a negative thought pattern. It's this thought pattern that feeds the lonely beast and keeps them stuck.

Teens: Our Most Lonely Age Group

"We live in a culture that seems to scorn basic needs for intimacy, closeness, and especially dependency while exalting independence."

—Amir Levine and Rachel Heller from *Attached*

It's 2018. We supposedly have the most technologically, psychologically, and medically advanced country on the planet. We say we understand what it means to be free and independent. Yet, our youth are suffering from an epidemic of loneliness, cloistered in their bedrooms or behind their screens like wounded, caged cubs whose environment is too dangerous to exist in long-term. Unlike the defenseless cubs' danger of being eaten by another wild animal, the danger for our teens is that of rejection and further isolation— the modern version of annihilation. For many teens, it is safer to stay in the confines of their rooms and behind the veil of their screens, where adults and peers cannot tease or chastise them for having emotional needs. But their loneliness becomes depression, and their depression seems to be manifesting in skyrocketing suicide rates for this neglected age group, likening their predicament to that of the wounded cub whose life is on the line in an untamed, ruthless environment.

The generations before haven't protected this current generation of teens. Instead, we've led them to believe that having "followers" on Instagram or Tumblr means you're connected and, therefore, should be happy. Schools have handed them iPads and laptops, insisting this is the way to learn and study in the twenty-first century. Equipped with addictive devices to hide behind, teens don't have to interact with kids in person as much. If they're lonely despite their social media following, they blame themselves for their emotional pain. If they have become socially anxious as a result of decreased face-to-face interaction, they feel weak and stupid.

Then there are the teens who *don't* have many "followers" or "likes" on social media. They may even be cyberbullied, which, for many, can confirm the distorted thinking that they are misfits who don't belong in today's society. This can lead to depression as well as, in some instances, suicide. One recent study out of the University of Pennsylvania discovered that when college students limited their social media time to less than thirty minutes a day, they were less lonely and less depressed.

The authors of the book *Attached* state: "We are only as needy as our unmet needs." In other words, the need for acceptance and connection is not only normal, it is vital to our ability to emotionally and physically thrive. If we are brainwashed into thinking that independence is equal to not needing others, we set ourselves up for feeling like failures. This is the paradox of our American culture's view on independence. This is the plight of our current youth. It's an old-fashioned view to think that emotionally attending to another's needs is coddling them or inhibiting their development in some way.

But what about the argument that our millennials are crippled by narcissism (a recipe for loneliness) because we *have* coddled them? Is this true for the z gens as well? The belief here is that by over-focusing on kids, by giving them medals and awards for merely participating in a sport or science fair, we have programmed them to expect accolades for doing virtually nothing. Some believe that we've indulged the millennial generation by rescuing them from discomfort and feeding their desires. However, while coddling may have been part of the helicopter parent's mode of operation, it is different than interdependence. And the latter is essential if we want to combat loneliness. Let me break this down.

Interdependence requires we be responsive to each other's needs, that we recognize and understand them. It doesn't connote rescuing. For example, if a child throws a tantrum because he has to leave the park and doesn't want to, we can reflect his inner experience of disappointment and show compassion for his frustration without usurping our goal to leave the park. We can soothe, but we don't indulge the child's desire to stay. Coddling would entail giving in to the tantrum and allowing the child 30 or more minutes at the park, even if it is inconvenient. The former creates connection between two people, therefore, preventing loneliness while the latter creates power over the parent, which is isolating for the child and can breed loneliness. While the former requires seeing and understanding, the latter only requires an emotional reaction that fails to convey an understanding of either party.

Jean Twenge, PhD has studied the narcissistic tendencies of what she calls the "me generation," (the millennial generation). She's found that, unlike previous generations, the "me generation" is more extrinsically motivated by money, fame, and external achievement as opposed to intrinsically motivated by purpose or meaning. Is this a result of supposed coddling? Or is it a result of social media, a platform that allows people to create whatever image they want to portray without having to be vulnerable? Or, is it a result of an unstable economy that left little hope for jobs in this country as many millennials came into the workforce during the height of the recession?

All theories are possible. In fact, all three phenomena have likely contributed to loneliness in our young adults. However, the jury is still out as to whether the z generation (which encompasses most of our teens today) is suffering from loneliness for the same reasons. Z gens have never been without technology and social media, and these two have gotten in the way of their having to form in-person relationships. It's not that teens today desire these in-the-flesh interactions less. In fact, research shows they want to meet with friends and family in person and hang out behind the screens less. It's that parents and caregivers, teachers and administrators, may be using the electronic babysitter and the electronic teaching tool far too often. Eye to eye, empathic, and educational exchanges may be getting lost. So, what do we do?

Eye Contact and Touch: The Lost Science of Bonding with Your Baby (And Your Friends)

Albrecht Durer, Leonardo da Vinci, Rafael. These are all artists who painted famous images of the Madonna and Child, lovingly looking at one another as the mother (Madonna) cradles her baby. Too often today, we see the opposite—live images of mothers texting on their smartphones while breast-feeding their babies. I'm not criticizing mothers for doing this. We are all caught up in a rat-race, overloaded with information and at the mercy of our phones to one degree or another. But it is a fact that the crucial stage of development in the first year of life, greatly depends on an available and responsive parent who bonds with his or her baby via touch and eye contact. Touch and eye contact between human beings help grow the brain.

Remember, in Chapter Two, when I explained the infant-caregiver gaze? Remember how when adults and babies do this, the eyes of the parent tend to dilate giving him or her "belladonna" eyes, and that infants tend to experience pleasure in response to seeing enlarged pupils? The infant's pupils will then dilate in response to their caregiver's. In such an exchange, the baby often smiles. Of particular importance is the fact that dilated pupils in the baby tend to elicit caretaking behavior in the adult unconsciously, and that the brains of both baby and caregiver are activated and promoting growth.

You may also be aware of moments when, after a period of mutual gazing, the baby will avert her eyes and break the exchange. This is the baby's way of saying, "okay, that's enough now," as it attempts to regulate what can be intense emotion as a result of this intimate, nonverbal communication. It's important that the caregiver stay attuned to the baby's affective responses in order to mirror and, therefore, co-regulate the baby's emotional experience. In other words, if the baby averts his or her eyes in order to prevent emotional flooding, the caregiver should allow this break so the baby can calm itself. By mirroring the baby's stares, smiles, and facial backing off, the caregiver helps the baby's right brain develop. The right brain is essential in emotion regulation. It is also more connected to the body, and, therefore, the immune system than the left brain. It is the part of the brain that learns social connection and cooperation—a key part of the human experience and central to preventing loneliness later in life.

Most parents do not realize the powerful impact they have on their babies' brain development based on their emotional and facial attunement to their babies. It's astounding to think that some developmental disorders may be prevented by allowing the time and eye contact needed in order to help the infant with emotion regulation and immune system development. But if a parent's gaze is often at her smartphone screen and a baby is being electronically "babysat" by a screen of his own (say an iPad or TV screen), the baby will have a harder time learning the skill of empathy and may, instead, learn the habit of disengagement. We're seeing today that emotional empathy among our teens is declining.

Could the lack of infant/caregiver attunement be part of the problem? I don't doubt that it is. In fact, when parents are unaware and unattuned to their babies' emotional needs, these babies are at risk for developing an insecure-avoidant attachment. If this doesn't get repaired, these babies can grow up to appear self-absorbed, uncomfortable with intimacy, and claim not to need help. Does this sound like the generalizations of the "me generation?" Don't be fooled, while they may appear self-focused and lacking empathy toward others, those with an insecure-avoidant attachment are often painfully lonely.

I've said in my chapter on attachment theory that repair of a dysregulated exchange is a powerful elixir to the psyche. I've gotten to experience the impact of repair both in my own life, but also in the lives of my patients. When an elderly parent comes to his adult son (my patient) and apologizes in person, face-to-face, for the mistakes she made during her son's upbringing this can have an incredible anti-anxiety and anti-depressant effect on the patient (adult child.) In turn, when one of my patient's missteps with his own child and later goes back to acknowledge both this fact and the emotional impact it likely had, he is engaging the parts of his *and his child's* brain that are responsible for emotional intimacy. Why? Because the brain is *always* changing and growing, even beyond early childhood development. While infancy is a crucial time for initial brain development and attachment formation, having a *corrective emotional experience* also has proven to change the brain and psyche for the better. Allan Schore, PhD, neuroscientist out of UCLA states that mis-attunement between caregiver and child occurs approximately one-third of the time but that repair of the mis-attunement can be just as crucial as attunement itself.

However, if the same babies who were given iPads to occupy themselves during a parent's dinner with friends, spend their tween and teen years on a similar device, it would seem that they are particularly vulnerable to arrested development of the right brain which, in turn, can impair the development of secure attachment. It can be a vicious cycle. The teen who may be vaguely aware of emotional emptiness but has little practice at how to engage intimately with others, turns to the screen for soothing, and unknowingly perpetuates the arrested development in emotional attachment. Here you have a recipe for loneliness among the generations of kids, teens, and young adults who are guinea pigs in the era of personal device use.

Eye contact isn't the only potent tool by which we can promote healthy brain development. Touch is of equal importance. Touch elicits a natural opioid effect on humans as it releases the hormone oxytocin that serves to facilitate social bonding and increase pleasure. Touch also decreases the production of adrenocorticotropin (ACTH), a stress hormone that propels us into a state of fight or flight. Both oxytocin production and adrenocorticotropin reduction are helpful mediators in the face of chronic stress. A 2012 study out of UCLA studied the effect of massage on the production of oxytocin and reduction of ACTH. What researchers found was that participants who received massage (vs. participants who did not) had a significant increase in oxytocin and a significant decrease of ACTH. This is relevant because if we can learn to remain calm and cooperative amidst a stressful situation (which the production of oxytocin and reduction of ACTH help us do), we are less adversely affected by stress. While I will go into depth on the importance of these hormones in chapter nine, what is pertinent to stress and loneliness is the fact that our young people today are actually experiencing human touch less than previous generations. One wonders if these younger groups are less apt to engage in prosocial behavior as well as less able to calm themselves amidst a crisis because they aren't receiving the regulating effects of these hormones through touch.

Really? Young people don't touch one another as often as older adults? Well, studies now indicate that millennials are having less sex (roughly a 9 percent difference) than the previous Generation X and are getting together less in person than previous generations. (It's hard to give someone a reassuring hand on a shoulder or warm hug through a screen). This doesn't mean that millennials don't *desire* human touch. Several studies indicate that they do. So, what we have here is a continued desire for human touch but decreased access to it. That is a recipe for loneliness.

What is even more concerning is that we are losing day to day human interactions that involve regular eye contact and sometimes touch. Interactions with the bank teller, the grocery clerk (hello Amazon Go) and even your barista (many of us have one in Seattle) may all be slipping out of our daily existence and into the history books. Online banking, clerk-free shopping, and robotic servers are either here or on the horizon, leaving us with *less* opportunity for the human contact that is so essential for stress and loneliness reduction. Remember, stress can cause loneliness and loneliness can cause stress. Any way to intervene on this growing epidemic is key.

Can the Elderly Help Us?
(And, how can we look out for them?)

"Aging is not lost youth, but a new stage of opportunity and strength."
—Betty Friedan

We are fortunate enough to have on the planet a generation or two of people who experienced life without the distraction of television and computer chipped devices. We have on the planet elderly people who not only enjoy the art of storytelling but experienced it as a way of life growing up. As I write, my mother is ninety-six years old. Yes, she has a smartphone and she texts me—with emojis. While the smartphone gives us the illusion of more frequent communication than if we didn't have it, the truth is my mother and I talk on the phone far less than when she (and I, for that matter) didn't have such a device. She can't tell me stories on the smartphone and no emoji, however clever, can replace the intonation in her voice or her beautiful laughter.

I was in my hometown recently and decided to record some of my mother's childhood memories as she recalled them. Yes, the voice memo feature on my phone was definitely handy (one of the many positives of smartphones), but the in-person experience was heart-warming and emotionally moving. I watched her face as she recalled her sad feelings during the great depression, her delight at remembering seeing her aunt perform at a music club, her comforting recollection of her mother's traditional, German cooking. Older people know how to do this. They tell stories with facial expression and engagement and perhaps even a reassuring pat on the hand. Even my literary manager, a sophisticated man in his seventies, goes out of his way to have face-to-face meetings, albeit with a computer site designed for Skype-like meetings because, "I like to see people when I talk to them," he says.

A reported 6,000,000 Americans over the age of sixty-five live alone. Lonely elderly people are 64 percent more likely to develop dementia than elderly people who have social connection. Loneliness is life-sucking and puts us at risk, not just for dementia and other cognitive dysfunction, but for cardiovascular disease, decreased immune health, and early death. Remember *loneliness is a stressor and stress can be a silent killer.*

While teens and millennials apparently top the loneliness chart these days, the elderly aren't far behind. Wouldn't it be great if our millennials got together with "the Greatest Generation" and "the Silent Generation" folks and had tea? Well, I'm happy to see that this is already beginning to happen. At least in the UK. The Cares

Foundation, founded by Alex Smith, has made a mission of connecting the UK's two loneliest populations through a buddy system. The Foundation provides opportunity for the elderly and for young adults to essentially hang out with one another. It has connected thousands of seniors and millennials and, so far, has reportedly made quite an impact on their reported loneliness.

In the United States, an Australian-born organization referred to as "the men's shed" has started to take hold. While this organization is primarily for men and based on the idea that men talk to one another more easily if they are engaged in a project, it uses warehouses and donated tools and supplies to provide men with the opportunity to build and fix things. It's a gathering place for men who may be retired or alone. They connect, by working side by side, shoulder to shoulder (as the organization explains) with other men. (I imagine they converse, too!)

Then there is an organization called Little Brothers—Friends of the Elderly. It's kind of like the Big Brothers and Big Sisters organizations only these volunteers are younger people volunteering to establish companionship with elderly people (vs. kids) who are alone. Again, it is the idea that uniting younger generations with older generations can benefit both and have an impact on everyone's loneliness.

It's simple, really, but think about it. The elderly may even help the younger generation to slow down in their hurried, overloaded lives. The younger generation can help the elderly get off the couch and dance, do art, or cook together. It really is a win-win and something we ought to think more seriously about how to make happen in any setting, from the corporate world to the community center.

Alleviating Loneliness (What to do and what not to do.)

Don't #1—In addressing loneliness, a danger that we must watch out for is indulging in the sexy new robotic industry to provide the lonely with robot companions. Professor Sherry Turkle has had a taste of what this looks like when she researched how the elderly (and their overworked adult children) responded to robot pets as companions. Adult children were eerily relieved as they felt the robot companion could alleviate them of some of the guilt they felt when not able to visit their elderly parents. And elderly people who were given the pet robot (otherwise known as Paro), spoke to and treated it as if it were real. Just because a robot is programmed to track your movements or look you in the eye doesn't mean it's capable of forming an attachment bond. Fake attachment, maybe, but not the real deal. I remind you that nothing can replace the value and importance of human touch, human eye contact, and human understanding of our pain, our joy, and our desire for relationship. While tempting for some, robots are no cure for loneliness.

Do #1—So, if robots don't cut the mustard for curing people's loneliness, what does? Well, the three organizations I referenced above may be a place to start. If the United States could support a national organization like Alex Smith's or an all-gender organization like the Men's Shed Association or a volunteer organization like Little Brothers, we might make some headway. If medical doctors could be trained to assess loneliness and have more places to refer their lonely patients to (other than the pharmacy for their anti-depressant) we may be able to calm the tsunami of loneliness in our country. (Theresa May calls this "social prescribing," and it is getting it underway in the UK) If, like the Australian government who allocated 46.1 million to a "community visitor's scheme," which connects younger and older people, we could help both the young and old with the significant stress loneliness causes. Or, if like the

British government, we appointed a "minister of loneliness" to lead varied projects to address our loneliness problem, we may make a dent in our loneliness epidemic. What you might do individually is volunteer for one of these organizations (people who volunteer are less lonely) and/or write your local congressperson to express your desire that US government address loneliness.

Don't #2—Manically fill the void. What I'm talking about here is loading up your schedule so that you are rarely home alone. You work at the office all day and schedule something every night of the week, be it pottery class, piano lessons, movie night and so on. Don't get me wrong. Engaging in activities that are novel or desired is definitely a good thing. But constant social engagement in order to avoid ourselves only makes it hard for us to learn how to be alone. Yes, we need to learn how to be alone with ourselves so that we aren't lonely when alone. If we run around like mad, saying yes to any social opportunity, not only will we exhaust ourselves, but we'll run the risk of still feeling lonely.

You may know what I'm talking about here. You are at a party with fifty or sixty people, a plate of food in your hand, chatting with an acquaintance, all the while not very interested in the conversation because you're putting on a face, pretending you have a full and happy life when, in reality, you feel lost and disconnected. On the other hand, you know if you stayed home you'd feel lonelier, so you disguise the loneliness by being out and continue to schedule being out a lot as it gives you the illusion of not being lonely. You wind up exhausted and still feeling empty. Why? Because you are simply *filling the void*. Let's look at the next "do" that could address the need for connection without overscheduling.

Do #2—Establish a loving relationship with yourself via *inquiring, accepting, and inner dialoguing* (IAI, not to be confused with AI!). Yes, alleviating loneliness starts with being alone. You have to know how to be *with* yourself when you are alone. This is different than just existing. Remember anxious and avoidant attachment styles? While the anxiously attached person may overschedule in the hope of finding others who can soothe their internal pain ("if only Johnny were here"), the avoidant may overschedule as a way of dismissing or avoiding his pain ("I've got to get out of here.") You have to know what is going on inside of you to know how to compassionately and lovingly respect and respond to it. Only looking for others to soothe you or running from your internal world won't help. Inquiring, Accepting and Inner Dialoguing entails 1) being still and asking yourself what you are feeling 2) accepting whatever you are feeling with compassion and 3) responding to the feeling with an internal dialogue of support. It may go something like this, "Jenny, what are you feeling right now?" "I'm feeling sad that I don't have a best friend." "I understand. Best friends can be great support and company. I can keep you company today." *Remember you are human, which means life isn't always smooth sailing. Inquiring, Accepting, and Inner Dialoguing will help you feel more connected to yourself.*

Loneliness researchers, the late John Cacioppo and his wife Stephanie Cacioppo found that the most effective strategy for decreasing loneliness was learning how to shift your inner dialogue to one that builds self-esteem rather than tears it down. In fact, it proved more powerful than volunteering or joining social groups. If you can't be vulnerable with yourself, and you can't be responsive to that vulnerability in yourself, you will have a hard time forming secure attachments with others. If you feel compassion and support coming from you to you, you are more likely to feel confident and engaged at that party and actually have a fulfilling experience.

Don't #3—Do not turn to social media. Contrary to popular belief this is not a fix for loneliness. Instead, it can perpetuate it. It is much better to get out and interact with a live human being rather than voyeuristically look in on others' lives, lives that have been constructed to erase flaws and appear fabulous. Social media surfing is false connection in that it provides people a platform in which they can put forward their best selves. While it does allow us to connect with long lost friends or new friends via shared interests or stories, it poses a risk to the lonely person who already has concluded that others have it together and she does not. Social media, in its tendency to mask flaws and superficially announce "achievements," can make the lonely person feel even more inadequate and, therefore, less likely to go out into the world and engage. Instead, read the next "do."

Do #3—Drop the mask. This entails vulnerability, not just with yourself, but with others. People who are lonely feel incredibly self-conscious as they've usually bought into the idea that something must be wrong with them if they don't have a partner, a family, or many friends. This causes them to isolate even further with their critical selves or, when out, to lie. But, if you've begun to practice being with yourself lovingly (above), then you are starting to build more confidence in yourself. You may not feel as sturdy as an oak tree, but if you know that you'll be there for yourself no matter what, that you won't criticize your emotional or circumstantial experience, but compassionately accept and respond to it, then you'll feel less intimidated by others—specifically, less intimidated by what you think they may be thinking of you.

If you learn to support yourself, you can speak genuinely when you are among other people, be they coworkers, party-goers or the grocery store clerk. I'm not saying that you have to pour out your sadness to every stranger you meet, but I am saying you can drop the superficial mask that you are an independent person without needs or difficulties. For example, if someone asks you what you did over the holidays, you can tell them that you are not close with family and, therefore, spent it alone, learning how to be with yourself. This doesn't have to be a sad confessional. This can be an upbeat, nonjudgmental, matter-of-fact yet open exchange. At least now you're talking vs. pretending.

I work with clients all the time on how to drop the mask, be who they are and tell the truth. It feels scary at first but is inevitably freeing. Instead of responding to a question about your new job with "it's great" when you're actually quite anxious about it, tell the truth, "I'm excited to have it, but am a little anxious learning the ropes." You'll either get an interested response and a real conversation will ensue, or you won't, and you'll move on to the next person all the while having the internal, positive and nonjudgmental support from yourself.

Don't #4—Don't engage in the negativity bias! The negativity bias is our tendency as humans to watch for threats in our environment. We learned this in ancient times when being aware of the bear in the bush was a life or death skill. However, with evolution, being hyper-aware of death threats isn't as relevant. But lonely people tend to perceive the world as full of rejection and criticism, and therefore, threatening and dangerous. This keeps lonely people isolated, as they are intimidated by the assumption that others' aren't interested in them or see them as undesirable. You may not realize how often your mind contemplates a potential threat and how little it notices ease, joy, and comfort. Lonely people's minds tend to bypass moments of connection and magnify moments of disconnection. "He frowned at me" is going to be more common in the lonely mind than "he smiled at me." To help you stop doing this, read the following "do."

Do #4—Practice happiness. Now that you've begun to speak compassionately and positively toward yourself, you can begin to implement strategies from the happiness researchers. Lonely people aren't typically happy. Happiness research has discovered measurable strategies for increasing your overall happiness which, in turn, will affect your internal confidence, thereby affecting the quality of your exchanges with others and your loneliness level.

I address some of these strategies individually and in more detail throughout the book but summarize them here: 1) *Get out in nature and let yourself experience awe.* Looking at a majestic mountain range, a star-filled sky, beautiful cloud formations, a fall tree decreases the stress hormone cortisol and increases a sense of well-being, particularly the feeling of being a part of something greater—the very feeling lonely people are missing. 2) *Offer physical affection* to those who are in your circle or receive it via the healing touch of therapeutic massage. I am not talking about sexual exchanges. I'm talking about platonic touch. Physical affection such as a hug to your sibling, an arm around a coworker's shoulder, a stroke of your child's head all increases oxytocin (otherwise known as the social connection hormone that makes us feel happier.) Or give your body the calming effect of therapeutic massage. One study indicated that those who received therapeutic massage had a greater sense of well-being 3) *Meditate* (there are myriad apps that can teach you how) It will increase your connection to yourself and your sense of well-being. 4) *Keep a gratitude journal.* The magic number here is *once a week* take notice, contemplate, and document something for which you feel grateful. 5) *Help others* (whether it be volunteering or simply picking up someone's dropped keys). Doing so will make you feel happier and less lonely. 6) As psychologist and happiness expert, Rick Hanson, says, *"Look for the good."* Be intentional about finding the good things in your day, anything from the comfort of a warm cup of coffee to the smile of a stranger. Notice these small moments, dwell on them long enough to soak them up so that your brain begins to *notice* good, instead of overlooking it.

6

THE FAST TRACK OF TECHNOLOGY

"Overwhelmed by the volume and velocity of our lives, we turn to technology to help us find time. But technology makes us busier than ever and ever more in search of retreat."

—Sherry Turkle, PhD, psychologist, researcher, author

tech-nol-o-gy *(noun):* machinery and equipment developed from the application of scientific knowledge

My husband and sons happily gave me an Apple Watch for Christmas one year. It was supposed to receive calls even if I didn't have my iPhone on me—they thought it was handy to always be reachable. Hmmm. "You don't have to have your phone on the ski slopes, Mom!" my older son informed me, believing it would be one less item for me to have to stuff in my slim-fit ski jacket. He was right. The watch was a lighter, more portable form of communication while skiing—as long as it worked, which it did for two months and then stopped. This forced me to make numerous calls to my cellular carrier and visit the Apple store before someone could figure out what was going on. Owning technology means managing technology.

Then there is the learning of technology. It's tiring to *have* to learn new technology as frequently as we do. When Windows came out with the cumbersome Windows 8, many complained that it was too different from the last version and not very user-friendly. But, if you bought a new PC, you were pretty much stuck with it. Even when we replaced cable TV with DIRECTV, my husband and I couldn't find the time to read the manual. All too often, we sheepishly handed the remote to our eighteen-year-old who would get the channel or movie more quickly than we ever could.

It's stressful to be in relationship to technology, much of the day, every day, remembering passwords, changing passwords, and figuring out security measures to protect ourselves from hacking. Our relationship to our country became a bit less secure when Eric Snowden revealed how much the government used technology to spy on us. It suffered a little more when the Facebook scandal broke, alerting users to the fact that data from approximately 87 million people had been illegally shared with Cambridge Analytica for improper use. It breaks even more when insurance companies inform us of a hack job that has left our medical information, including Social Security numbers, in the wrong hands. Whose hands it's in, exactly, is never really clear. The more our lives are lived on, *and through*, technology, the more vulnerable we become. We feel less safe as anything can be hacked—our email, our bank accounts, our utility and transportation systems—all of which contribute to an insecure attachment to our nation.

And then there are the effects of tech use on our relationships. We're more distracted as we try to respond to the multitude of ways people ping us. We look up less as we're too busy looking down. We eat while emailing and walk while texting. We're more disconnected from one another. The group that takes the hardest hit is our teens. They've never *not* had technology. It's been in their parents' hands or their own since they were born. Teens also use tech more than they need to as smartphones, in particular, not to mention video games, can be highly addictive. And, overuse of technology is concerning as it has been associated with increased dry eye, poor sleep, difficulty staying on task, anxiety, depression, and even suicidal thoughts. Let's look at why.

Screens, Teens, and the Brain

"The benefits of technology can still be realized, but the health impact of screen-based technology needs to be taken much more seriously, particularly when it comes to our most vulnerable citizens—our children."

—Victoria Dunckley, MD, psychiatrist/author

Alex, an eleven-year-old boy, diagnosed at age seven with dyslexia and ADHD, was constantly moving. He needed to be engaged in something, not just anything, but something novel at all times. If he wasn't, he'd walk around the house repeatedly stating, "I'm bored, I'm bored," driving his parents crazy as they felt pressured to come up with things for Alex to do. Given his executive functioning challenges, his parents made sure Alex was in a school that understood his difficulties, and that didn't require laptops or iPads. Technology, particularly screen addiction, is something ADHD kids are more susceptible to because the constant stimulation of the screen boosts dopamine—a hormone that helps with motivation and mood and which is often low or dysregulated in kids with ADHD.

The iPad and phone Alex *did* have, had no games downloaded and were only to be used at home under specific circumstances. Alex's parents saw what gaming apps and consoles had done to some

105

of his friends—turned them into behaviorally challenging kids who argued and threw tantrums on a near-daily basis. So, they wanted the devices he did own to be essentially game-free. But, when Christmas came along and the family was gifted a PlayStation 4, they allowed Alex to try it out.

Alex's mother's plan was to teach him how to moderate his time on games by having him use the timer on his phone as a stopping point reminder. (Using technology to curb technology use is a thing these days.) She felt that by giving her son the power to learn regulation, he'd be better off and less likely to tantrum than if she rigged the device so that it would automatically shut off at a designated time, something other parents in Alex's friend group had done. It didn't take a week before she realized self-monitoring was not going to work—Alex had become addicted to *Fortnite* (an engaging survival action game that was like *crack* for tweens and teens). Anytime his parents noticed that he hadn't turned off the console at the agreed-upon time, he'd argue, "I can't stop now, I'm in the middle of a game!" But here was the problem: *all* Alex wanted to do was play *Fortnite*. He didn't want to go to soccer practice anymore; he didn't want to attend family events anymore. In fact, he didn't want to do anything that had previously interested him—one of the sure signs of game addiction.

One day, when his mother firmly told him that he was done playing, Alex lost it. Now, while tantrums aren't uncommon for kids with executive functioning issues, by eleven years old, Alex had grown out of them. "It's scarier when an older kid tantrums," his mother said. "Alex was eleven and a half and *big*. He looked out of control. He started throwing things and broke something—I don't remember what—but I knew that was it," she recalled. "I took his phone and told him the PlayStation was going away. He begged and pleaded, but my husband and I had reached our limit and said it was gone for at least the rest of the school year." Alex's parents kept their promise. For the remainder of the school year, Alex repeatedly asked for the game console back, but his parents didn't give in.

Then summer came, and Alex's parents were lucky enough to have gotten a last-minute spot at an out-of-state, outdoor camp for dyslexic kids. It was a six-week program. Alex was wary about being gone from home that long, as were his parents, but they felt he needed a completely different environment that would be open to outdoor activity and away from the temptation of digital devices. With trepidation and hope, Alex's father took him to the camp and within a week, it was clear that Alex loved the camp! He swam, hiked, biked and essentially lived for outdoor adventures.

When Alex came home that August, he was a changed boy. "There was a calmness about him, things just rolled off his back," his mother says. "He could look us in the eye, he wasn't moving about all the time, he wasn't saying he was bored anymore. The camp was magic." When asked what she thought had happened in those six weeks to have such an impact on Alex, his mother replied, "I think six weeks in the outdoors without digital devices (including smartphones) changed his brain." I'm sure the face to face social interaction helped too.

At the time of my conversation with Alex's mother, it had been six months since he'd returned from the camp. His mood and temperament had remained calm. He had told his mother he wasn't interested in gaming anymore and took up biking, meeting friends at the park, and entertaining himself with creative endeavors. His imagination flourished, and his nervous system quieted. Alex's mother is grateful to have stuck to her guns and to have found the camp. Not only did it help Alex kick his gaming addiction, it changed his hyperactivity, his difficulty focusing, and his challenge with regulating emotion.

How could simply putting down a game controller and spending time in the outdoors change a person's brain? It's true that nature calms the nervous system, reducing the stress hormone cortisol within minutes. It's also true that digital devices (in some ways, the antithesis of nature) do the opposite—they tend to raise cortisol levels. They also tap into dopamine, the reward center of the brain that brings pleasure, and, sometimes, addiction.

According to research conducted by Common Sense Media, a San Francisco based nonprofit organization that provides advocacy for safe technology use for families, the average teen spends nine hours a day on screen media. You heard that right...most of a teenager's waking hours are reportedly spent on a screen, 46 percent of which is on mobile devices. Once you get past two hours, you're well on your way to spending too much time on screens according to Jean Twenge, PhD, a psychology researcher out of California State University, San Diego. Her research indicates that when kids spend more than two hours a day on screens, they are less happy than kids who don't. A new, long-term study funded by the National Institute of Health, published initial results that kids who spent more than two hours a day on screens got lower scores on thinking and language tests than kids who spent less than two hours a day on screens.

The American Academy of Pediatrics recommends families make a "media use plan" designed for their specific child. But, even with a media use plan, parents of this generation don't have total control over their kids' screen use or the time to monitor it. Alex's parents tried this without success. Plus, devices are highly accessible through friends and even required in many schools.

Project Tomorrow reported just five years ago, in 2014, that one-third of middle and high school students were using devices provided by their schools. Years ago my husband attempted to put parental controls on a school-required device so our then-seventh grader wouldn't stumble upon pornography or violent YouTube videos. The next day, we got an exasperated call from our son during math class, stating that his instructor needed him to access an app—that was unrated and, therefore, blocked—for class. While we eventually figured out how to get the right amount of control without having to okay each app, one by one, it hasn't been without research and it doesn't protect kids from everything. In fact, it's time-consuming to determine how to protect kids from the dark side of tech without isolating them from their peer group or school community. Some families give up entirely because their tech-savvy kids know how to turn off the parental control or Wi-Fi monitoring device, anyway.

Yes, mobile devices, especially smartphones, can increase learning opportunities and bring ease to some parents, despite the stress they cause. Many parents like the fact that kids can easily email their teacher with a question or participate in online homework chats. Some parents are comforted by the fact that they can *track* their child via the smartphone, which lets them know where their child is at any given time. Others are relieved that tweens and teens have an accessible way to call home or reach 911. But, how often do kids actually use the device for those purposes? Studies show that tweens primarily use their smartphones for media and that 43 percent of teens use them for video-watching.

In 2018, I began to notice a slew of flyers coming to my office for continuing education events. I get flyers weekly for various workshops or courses, but what stood out over the course of several months was that the workshop topics centered on kids' emotional and behavioral problems: *Oppositional, Defiant and Disruptive Children and Adolescents: Non-Medication Approaches to the Most Challenging Behaviors; Over 75 Quick, On-the-Spot Techniques for Children and Adolescents with Emotional and Behavioral Problems; Treating Anxiety Disorders in Children and Adolescents; Self-Regulation in Children: Keeping the*

109

Body, Mind, and Emotions on Task in Children with Autism, ADHD, or Sensory Disorders; Trauma-Informed Compassionate Classrooms: Strategies to Reduce Challenging Behavior, Improve Learning Outcomes and Increase Student Engagement; Suicide and Self-Harm in Adolescents; Effective Techniques for School Refusal Behavior." I don't see kids and adolescents in my practice and yet flyers like these found my mailbox and outnumbered workshop flyers for adults three to one. Why is there such a need for clinicians to address child and adolescent behavior these days? What's driving the market for these courses?

Victoria Dunckley, MD, would say it's screen addiction. In her book, *Reset Your Child's Brain,* Dunckley informs us of her own empirical research—the calming effect screen abstinence can have on kids' emotional, psychological, and behavioral well-being, much like what Alex and his parents experienced when they isolated him from screens and put him in nature for six weeks. Dunckley purports to greatly reduce, if not eradicate, many of the neurological, psychological, and behavioral problems listed in the afore-mentioned flyers by getting kids to abstain from all screen use for just four weeks. Even to those of us who didn't grow up with smartphones and tablets, a four-week digital abstinence feels daunting. After all, adults aren't immune to the same tech addiction that plagues teens. In a Time Mobile Poll, reportedly 84 percent of people worldwide say they couldn't go a day without their mobile phone.

But Dunckley's experience with her patients reflects the findings of several studies—that heavy exposure to screens of any kind can cause brain damage in children and teens. You heard that right. Studies now show that excessive screen time (approximately seven hours a day, which we know many kids and teens meet) reduces gray matter in the brain. Gray matter is responsible for many of our executive functions such as planning, organizing, completing tasks, as well as controlling socially unacceptable impulses. Then there are the studies that correlated excessive screen use with damage to the insula (the part of the brain responsible for empathy—the ability to step into another person's shoes.) This finding echoes Jean Twenge's studies that indicate that our millennial generation seems to care less about others and more about themselves.

It seems that the only children who are *not* adversely affected by screen use are the ones that use them less than two hours a day. Where did the researchers find those kids anyway? They seem to be a rare bunch.

Solutions for Kids and Teens Screen Use
The very young

It is not recommended that children eighteen months old or younger be exposed to screens, period. It inhibits their development. It is also recommended that children ages two to five spend no more than one hour a day on screens, which includes television and playing with mommy's smartphone!

No TV or Game Consoles in the Bedroom

Studies show that kids who have TVs or game consoles in their rooms get less sleep and are exposed to more violent conduct. It's not surprising that these same kids are then more aggressive than kids who don't have these screens in their rooms. Make this rule number one—no TV or game console in your child's room.

Hold off on Hand-Held Devices

Kids younger than twelve are usually with their parents, teachers, or other adults and there really isn't a good reason for them to have their own smartphone (and there are several reasons they shouldn't). One exception is a child of divorced parents or a single-parent household. Landlines are becoming obsolete and being home alone

111

without a phone to contact an adult may make that child feel anxious. If a phone can reduce anxiety and keep a kid safe, that's a good thing. But keep in mind, that phone doesn't have to be a smartphone.

Hand-held devices are addictive, much like a drug can be. This leads to excessive device use which isn't good for the brain and body. What's more, younger kids can easily have hand-held devices in their rooms, at other kids' houses, or at school, which means controlling their screen time is harder and taking the device away can result in frustrating and unnecessary struggle. And, devices without parental controls are windows to the internet, which means access to a host of adult content children's brains are not ready to process.

Charge Devices in a Neutral Location at Night

Having hand-held devices plugged into your child's room at night can present too much temptation when they're supposed to be sleeping, not to mention the disruptions caused by the dinging and buzzing when they forget to turn them off. While I do believe older teens need to learn to manage their own screen use, especially as they get ready to go off to college where no one will be monitoring them, younger teens still need help in reducing the temptation. My fourteen-year-old has to plug in his devices in the kitchen; whereas, my eighteen-year-old, who is more disciplined based on age, keeps them in his room. If you allow the latter and find that your child is sneaking the phone at night, don't reprimand or blame him. Remember, devices are addictive, and kids can't help that. Simply change the rule that devices will now be plugged in outside the bedroom.

Require Physical Activity

Devices are making kids more sedentary than ever. This puts them at risk for a host of physical problems later in life, including cardiovascular disease, diabetes, and other metabolic diseases. If you want your child to be on a screen less, require she do something active every day. For younger kids, you can make a game out of this by charting their physical activity time and rewarding them with something special (just not screen use). For older kids, sports are good in that they require practices and games that automatically build in physical activity. Let kids choose the activity and include choices such as dance, drama, martial arts, or anything that involves physical movement.

Take the Time to Research and Set Parental Controls

It only takes one time of logging onto a pornography site to realize why this is important. Without parental controls, kids are exposed to everything and anything via the internet. Seeing violent or pornographic sexual images at young ages can be traumatizing. I've had many a patient who was exposed to adult content at a young age and remembers it like it was yesterday, wishing they could get the images out of their head. While kids will still have access to devices, such as their friend's device, which may not screen out this content, the likelihood of stumbling upon it before their brains can understand it is reduced when you set controls. And don't forget to put passwords on *your* devices, so they can't freely access content on any other device in the house.

Model for Your Child or Teen

If you're on your device all the time, unavailable for eye-to-eye conversations, your kid will be, too. If you eat your breakfast and text at the same time, chances are your teen will, too. Interest, understanding, compassion can all be communicated through the eyes, and all can release oxytocin in the brain (the hormone of social connection). As much as it appears that teenagers are uninterested in, and annoyed by their parents, research shows that they need and want our help. Making the excuse that your teen is on his phone isn't a reason to be on yours. Be the first to put it away and engage him. Establish device-free times or places, like mealtimes, car rides (not a good idea to mix phones and automobiles, anyway), events (including sports games), and/or two hours before bed. Reducing the places and times that phones are allowed for *anyone and everyone* in the house increases the chance that family members will be more present, more connected, less stressed, and less lonely.

Talk to Your Child or Teen

I know this sounds obvious but talking to our children has become less frequent than it used to be. The fact that most families need both parents employed in order to stay afloat means that kids have less time with their parents. Add in the ever-present smartphone or laptop, and now eye-to-eye communication is reduced even more. While teens may often reject parental input, underneath the entitled attitude is a vulnerable being who is trying to navigate relationships, school, and extra-curricular activities while trying not to look foolish. You don't need to bombard them with information or incessant questions, but you can talk to them about anything from sex to sailboats. Doing so in a caring, nonjudgmental way without a device in hand, will render the best results.

Know the Signs of Depression, Anxiety, and Suicidal Ideation

Depression in kids and teens often looks different than it does in adults. While they may have the same symptoms of apathy, sleeping too much or too little, hopelessness, appetite changes and feeling helpless to affect their circumstances, they are also likelier to present with more than usual irritability. Yes, tweens and teens are naturally irritable, but depressed tweens and teens are highly irritable. Look for constant argumentativeness, unwillingness to engage in conversation, increased anger, tantrums, and a generally dysphoric mood. Whatever you do, do not minimize their problems or tell them to look on the bright side. This can make them feel worse as they kick themselves for not being happy when you think they should be. If you think your child is depressed, get them professional help.

Anxiety in kids and teens can also be slippery to identify. Look for the more obvious symptoms of stated worry, upset stomach, and avoidance of things that feel scary to your child. But also pay attention to withdrawal from others (your child may be avoiding social situations that make him anxious), irritability (anxiety is hyperarousal of the central nervous system which can manifest in a state that looks like irritability or hyperactivity) and defiance or opposition as these may be symptoms that your child is trying to avoid a stressor. If a child is hell-bent on not going to school or to a sports event, approaching him with "tough love" by making him go, risks misunderstanding the possible underlying cause of his or her opposition (possible fear or worry). Telling them they shouldn't worry is not helpful. Empathize and get them help.

Suicidal Ideation is becoming increasingly common among teenagers and even younger children these days. Pay attention to suicide risk signs, such as social withdrawal from or conflict with peers or family members, falling grades or other academic struggles, being bullied, feeling worthless, giving away belongings, thinking they are a burden, talking about not being around, apathy, isolation, anger, and drug or alcohol use. If your child presents with any of these symptoms, don't assume he is just having a bad day. Take him seriously. Give him a nonjudgmental presence so he knows he can come to you for help. Let him know he isn't alone, that many others have felt this way, that there are solutions, and then get him professional help. Make sure your child or teen knows how to access school counselors and crisis lines. I know it is scary to admit your child may feel suicidal, but the perceived comfort of denial isn't worth risking a life.

Social Media, For Better or Worse

"We are driven to fabricate an enemy as a scapegoat to bear the burden of our denied enmity."

—Sam Keen, social psychologist and author

Julia is fourteen years old. She lives in a small town in the Midwest and loves sports. Julia meets people easily and spends many weekends shooting hoop at her local sports center. But, despite having an iPad and smartphone since fifth grade, she's never been on social media. Her parents don't allow it. When she hit middle school and saw most of her friends were glued to their phones ogling over whatever was trending on Instagram, she begged her parents for an Instagram account, but they said "no." In fact, they said "no" repeatedly. While this angered Julia initially, it didn't take long for tragedy to hit and for Julia to get completely turned off from social media.

A boy in her town was dared by a group of girls over social media to kill himself if his girlfriend did it. While exchanging dramatic messages, some girls told the boy that his girlfriend just went to kill herself (which wasn't true). He believed it and killed himself in response. The incident shocked and deeply saddened Julia. The entire community was "shaken" as she put it, trying to understand how such an egregious incident could've occurred in what felt like a safe town where everyone knew everyone. After that, Julia stopped asking her parents for social media accounts.

Julia's mother attests to the fact that not having access to social media hasn't been easy for her daughter. But even though Julia

116

misses out on social plans sometimes as a result of not having access to group chats, she has accepted her parents' rule. She gets her socializing the old-fashioned way—by joining sports teams, calling or texting other kids, and by hanging out with her mom, watching sitcoms.

Julia says she prefers this to "stressing out over the latest drama on Snapchat." In fact, when she heard through her friends that she was being bullied online ("I'm an easy target because I'm not on social media," she says), she didn't let it get to her. "I was like, 'whatever,' because I didn't actually see it," Julia reports. Julia's mother adds that when Julia is bashed online, "it fizzles fast because she doesn't relive the drama all night long by reading the cyber message over and over. She also doesn't respond to it." Julia concurs:

"There's a lot of drama, like when someone says something bad to someone, they aren't saying it to their face where it can be dealt with right then and there, between those two people—on Snapchat they can screenshot it and then everyone can see what the person said, and pretty soon the whole school knows what's going on."

Paola, born in 1991, is of the millennial generation. She got her first iPhone when she was twenty-two, which was later than most of her friends. Prior to that, she remembers feeling left out as they all gathered around one another's phones, looking at Instagram, the largest social media platform for that age group at the time. "I just wanted to be talking about everything everyone was talking about on Instagram," she remembers. When Paola finally got an iPhone and her own Instagram page, she was now part of the scene. She stopped watching TV or doing much of anything else as she reports spending two to three hours a day trying to create the perfect photo or meme so as to gain followers.

"Why were followers so important?" I asked Paola.

"Because it was cool to have a lot of followers. It meant you were popular."

"When Snapchat came out, did you get on it?"

"For sure. Snapchat was cool because you could post a picture of what you were doing and send it to your friends right away. Everyone wanted to know what everyone else was doing, like especially with boys, you know. You could post a picture of some cool place you were or who you were with. It was a show-off thing."

"Did it incite jealousy?"

"For sure, I think it did with most people because it was like, wow, look where they are, I want to be there."

"Do you think the overall impact of being on social media made you feel better or worse about yourself?"

"I didn't realize it at the time, but it made me feel bad about myself. I was constantly comparing myself to others and I started to feel inadequate. It's why I eventually got off it."

Paola went on to say that in November of 2017, she deactivated all her social media accounts because it was taking so much time away from things that had become more important to her, like studying. "It distracted me from real life, and I got so tired of it." Once she took herself off all social media, Paola said she felt so much better, "I became more of an in-the-moment person, and it was interesting because I began to notice how much people were always on their phones, posting stuff. But even though I lost contact with a lot of people, I didn't miss it. I had so much more time!" she exclaims. "I worked out more. I hung out more with people in person. I studied more. My grades improved." When I inquired what it was like to hang out with friends who were still on social media, she said the following, "I began to notice how much anxiety they had, being on their phones, looking at stuff and being so distracted, but they didn't get it, they didn't see it."

Social media can bring out jealousy and meanness in people. Why is this? It's the "faces of the enemy" phenomenon I spoke about in Chapter Two. People feel protected behind a screen, free to facelessly rant or essentially let out the dark parts of themselves they otherwise repress, like how some of the kids were with their robotic toys in Sherry Turkle's study. Johnny would never tell Mary "you're a loser" to her face. But, online, he doesn't have to fear her wrath or feel guilty if she cries. He can just release his anger (which could have to do with his own feelings of worthlessness) onto the faceless person on the other side of town or wherever.

Approximately 43 percent of our tweens and young teens are cyberbullied and approximately 53 percent admit saying something mean to someone online. The majority of those cyberbullied (58 percent) do not tell their parents. The most common form of cyberbullying? A teen's smartphone.[47] The most common social media site teens use: Snapchat. And Snapchat has been proven to evoke more jealousy among its users than Facebook (a site known for making people feel poorly).

Studies show that just the "ping" of one's phone can release dopamine in the brain—the neurotransmitter that contributes to feelings of pleasure and activates reward-seeking behavior. If you send a provocative text or photo, you're likely to get more "pings" or "likes." Why would people want more "pings" or "likes"? Because people feel disconnected, lonely, and depressed these days and are likely looking for some spark, albeit superficial. High school teacher, Theodore Grover, calls his students' use of social media a "disconnected connection."

Julia's story of how teens are negatively impacted by social media is in line with Jean Twenge's research out of Cal State San Diego. In her studies on teen behavior and mental health across generations, the increase in loneliness and depression in iGens (another name for Generation Z) is closely related to the introduction of the smartphone and social media. No previous generation has shown such worrisome statistics.[48] Other studies corroborate this theory.[49] One study found that college students who reduced their social media time to thirty minutes a day were statistically and significantly less lonely and depressed.[50]

But it's not just teens that are suffering. Of all the clients who bring up topics in therapy related to their Snapchat, Instagram, or Facebook accounts, very few have positive experiences. Most client stories I hear about social media are related to something they saw, read, or were forwarded that made them feel inadequate. Take, for example, a client who is estranged from her father, but finds out via Facebook that her Dad was in town last week and never bothered to call. Or, there is the ongoing story of my client who can't stop herself from stalking an old boyfriend who is reportedly madly in love with someone new. His life is displayed in endless photos with his new flame—scantily clothed on a tropical beach, drinking beer in a bar, hanging out at a concert. "Why didn't he want to do those things with me?" she weeps. If she wasn't spending hours looking at these painful posts, would she feel this poorly?

Researcher Ethan Kross and colleagues found that the more their research subjects used Facebook, the less satisfied they were in the moment afterward. In addition, the more they used it over a two-week period (compared to subjects who used it less), the more their subjective sense of well-being declined. Essentially, Facebook is bad for your mood and outlook on life. Despite the popular notion that it enhances well-being through social connection, the research is telling us that Facebook use actually decreases your sense of well-being.[51,52] My clients' testimonies echo this fact.

120

So, why do we use sites like Facebook so much? With social media, a constant temptation to peek into other people's lives exists—a method of sleuthing that didn't exist before 2006, that is, before Facebook came on the scene. As you've read from statistics on happiness, loneliness, stress, and anxiety that I presented earlier in the book, many Americans are ill at ease. People are sleuthing because they want to feel better but don't realize the answer lies in healing their estranged connection to themselves, to each other (in Kross's study cited above, no one's well-being decreased from in-person social interactions), and to their nation.

Unfortunately, social media has become so pervasive, so expected, that people feel forced into participating in it in order to keep abreast professionally. Essentially, what most of us have learned in the last ten or more years is that we either embrace the social media scene or we'll be left out, unseen, not regarded as legitimate. It's concerning. There are many people in the world doing great things who don't necessarily want to "post" about it. Will they fall through the cracks and forfeit opportunities to those who are social media gurus?

There are some reports that indicate being on social media can help with loneliness, help educate people about things that can enhance their lives, and help people express themselves in ways they aren't able to do offline. One study out of the Johns Hopkins Bloomberg School of Public Health indicated that video gaming addiction and the depression it can cause in gamers seemed to be offset by whether gamers had a social media friend network or not. Those who did were less likely to show signs of addiction.[53] There are likely some benefits to social media, but it is definitely not a replacement for in-person connection, nor is it a cure for social anxiety.

I've given you some unsettling information about social media, not because I'm 100 percent against it, but because the expectation to be on it, the misuse of it, and the amount of time people spend reading and posting may be affecting our ability to develop intimate, compassionate relationships to ourselves and others. Perhaps, if we all vowed to use social media sparingly and for the better good, it could help us more than estrange us. Here are some tips on how to handle the dark side and bring out the potential of social media.

Tips to Reduce the Negative Impact of Social Media

Think Before You Tweet, Text, or Tap
Because the smartphone is essentially an appendage these days, and because social media posts happen throughout the day, it's easy to respond to something without thinking. It's easy to snap a photo and send it. It's easy to half-heartedly reply to a tweet like you're checking a mark on your to-do list that gives you the illusion of accomplishment or connection. It's harder, but more rewarding, to take the time to mindfully post or respond. I tell my clients that one of the best things they can do in life is to be thoughtful about what they say and do. I don't mean paranoid. I mean thoughtful. What do you feel? What is your aim? What will you have to gain by your action and will that gain hurt someone else? When we don't pay full attention, we tend to react. And, once the send button is hit, it's too late. So slow down. Think before you tweet, text, or tap. Tune in to yourself and others. And know that if you're tuned in, you're not missing out.

Use One Site Only
It's not surprising that people who are on multiple social media sites are more depressed than people who are on two or fewer. A recent

122

study out of the University of Pittsburgh's Center for Research on Media, Technology, and Health reported that people who are on seven to eleven social media platforms had a three times higher risk of depression than those who were on zero to two platforms. We don't know if more depressed people gravitate toward social media in the hope of connection or spark, or if the social media activity is causing the depression. But, even if depressed people are on social media more, research indicates it will only make them feel worse. So, if you are trying to make one rule for yourself, allow yourself just one social media platform. I realize this goes against some professional advice that you need to be visible across many platforms, but isn't this another case of our just getting caught up in cultural pressure to do something because we're threatened with missing out if we don't?

Post Something Kind

If you can't kick the habit of social media use because you feel it benefits you more than it harms you, make a pact with yourself to only use it for the better good. In other words, post quotes or stories that are compassionate and potentially helpful to others. Research shows that when we help other people, we feel happier. Instead of criticizing someone's Tweet or bashing someone's photo, why not compassionately reach out? Kind tweets might decrease stress and positively connect you to others.

Get Out in Nature

Nature is the opposite of technology. Just as all that buzzing, ringing, clicking, and radiation-emitting can amp us up, nature calms us. Just as tech use interrupts our focus, nature helps us regain focus. While overuse of technology narrows our visions, nature widens our perspectives.

People look at screens much of the day and evening, but they don't look at the trees, the flowers, the birds, the moon, the stars, the sky, the grass, the ocean, the river, the lake, the mountains and all the various creatures hopping, swimming, running, and flying around in earth's natural environment. When we cease to get out in nature because we're too busy scrolling through Instagram posts or answering the eighteenth email of the hour, we miss the endless wonder that lives right outside our doors, from the sun that peeks between skyrises in the city to the vast blue sky on the wide-open plains. What's more, when we fail to get out in nature because we don't want to miss a text or tweet, we lose an opportunity to reduce our stress and loneliness. Being in nature can ease our minds and bodies and remind us that mother earth is a companion.

It really doesn't take much. You can stand in the middle of your street and watch the clouds gently float across a summer sky. You can ponder the delicate feet of a blue jay as it perches on a park tree branch. You can walk barefoot in the sand and listen to the ocean waves. From five minutes to five hours, soaking up nature can take as little or as much time as you choose.

AI: Helpful or Hurtful?

"AI is a fundamental, existential risk for human civilization."

—*Elon Musk*

In 2017, when my son was a junior in high school, he gave a TEDx Talk at his school. The topic: Artificial Intelligence.

"What's the gist of your speech?" I asked him.

"That artificial intelligence will improve the world," he said.

"But what about the idea that robots could begin to think for themselves and do some damage?"

"Humans can add limitations to that," he replied.

'What about the idea that people could have less face-to-face contact and, therefore, struggle with how to have intimate relationships?"

"People will have more opportunity for intimate relationships because the technology will allow more people to talk face to face virtually, and transportation speeds will increase, allowing people to see each other more easily."

Hmmm, talking "face to face virtually" doesn't sound intimate to me and traveling a bunch seems to disrupt relationships more than nurture them. But what do I know? My generation was all about face to face, open communication. My high school conducted intimate group talks to deal with teenage emotional struggles. I remember listening to peers pour their hearts out in these sessions and feeling respect for them. Before the group, many of us had incorrect assumptions about each other. After the group, those who were enemies became friends. I distinctly remember feeling less alone and emotionally safer at school because of this face-to-face opportunity.

But teens today aren't comfortable sharing their feelings face to face with one person, let alone a group. Even though research shows that group therapy can be a successful form of treatment for adolescents, most schools do not make it available for their students. And, students are so locked into their digital form of communication, to look up and into someone's eyes is unnatural for many. Digital communication doesn't necessarily build trust. In fact, given the prevalence of cyberbullying, not to mention persona-building through social media, mistrust and betrayal are common experiences for teens today.

Smartphone addiction has already proven to increase social isolation, anxiety, and depression. What impact could artificial intelligence have on the social world of this Z Generation

125

(sometimes referred to as the iGeneration)? Are teens today bracing themselves for the inevitable: that, like it or not, one day, intelligent robots will work alongside them, becoming their colleagues, companions, rivals, and maybe even part of their brains? Or, are teenagers enamored with the idea that one day robots can clean their houses, run their errands, and cook their meals so they can have more time to pursue their goals?

What I do know is that teenagers today, like any generation, are trying to figure out how to have a good life. I also know that adolescent dystopic literature abounds, reminding teens that it is their generation's plight to save the world. My older son's high school English class one year was aptly called "Literature of the Apocalypse," and my younger son's knowledge of drone warfare and artificially intelligent weaponry is eye-opening. Why does he know so much? Because a teenager's favorite pastime is watching YouTube videos, and there are more than nine million YouTube videos (today) on robotic warfare. When I asked my son about robotic warfare, he said this:

"It's good in some ways because we can protect ourselves against enemies that don't have this kind of weaponry. At the same time, it's bad because it could get out of hand and destroy entire regions of the world."

"How do you feel about the future of robots in general?"

"It's exciting," he replied. "It means we're progressing and evolving."

"But what if it goes poorly?"

"Well, it could go poorly if we create ones that are too powerful or too smart and they become destructive instead of helpful."

"Given that it could go poorly, do you still think AI is worth it?"

"Yeah, because we can also do a lot of good things. Robots could make us less vulnerable by helping us medically, and they can get tasks done much faster…you know, like interactive walls."

"No, I don't know. What would be on the walls?"

"Just watch the video, Mom."

Watching videos is less work than using one's imagination. It's also less work than having to explain something to your mom. Videos are one of the reasons screen addiction has become so pervasive and why our patience with each other is waning. Could this decreased knowledge of how to communicate intimately and patiently lead the Z Gens to welcome robots as colleagues and companions?

Sherry Turkle, a clinical psychologist, author, and MIT professor, has spent her career researching the effects of artificial intelligence on humans. In her book, *Alone Together,* she discusses the allure of robot companions for the elderly, robot babysitters for the young, and robot partners for the lonely. Many people in her long-term study liked these robot buddies. Children played with them like imaginary friends, their relationship extending a bit beyond the usual transference kids project onto stuffed animals. For example, when one group of kindergartners sees that their sociable robot, Furby, is breaking down, they immediately assume Furby's "sick and frantically try to "operate" on it with mixed emotions.

The Furby toy responds to human interaction and even adjusts its personality according to how one treats it. Do these features of the robot help kids understand ethical behavior toward humans? If the Furby looks sad or yells, "ouch" if you hurt it, does that trigger a human being's conscience to treat it better? Turkle observed that kids were more likely to treat Furby and a similar sociable robot called "My Real Baby" aggressively because they could. They wouldn't get in trouble for unleashing their inner shadows as they knew the toys were just machines. Is this okay, or is it dangerous?

In a 2017 *CNN* article, Sherry Turkle, warned, "You yell at Alexa…you know Alexa is a machine…we treat machines as though they were people. And then, we are drawn into treating people as though they were machines." This concept proves to have some legs when sociable robots are used as companions or caregivers. While it may be alluring to hire a robot to keep your elderly mother company because you can't visit her often enough to keep her from feeling alone, it is an overly practical decision that seems to forget that humans need humans. Surprisingly, Turkle found that many millennials who were asked about robot caretakers for the elderly said they were all for it. They saw the hiring of a robot to interact with elderly parents as helpful. Remember, true attachment depends on the human brain. It takes trusting relationships with people and people-to-people engagement to help grow resilience.

Despite this fact, in another study, lonely millennials felt that talking to a chatbot (or robot psychotherapist) helped them feel listened to and understood. As much as a robot may be able to learn some of the simpler techniques of, say, Rogerian client-centered therapy, a part of which includes, you, the therapist repeating back to the patient what you heard him say, it is impossible for a robot to *care* about what the patient is saying. Robots don't *care* about people, and people need to feel not only listened to but cared about. Feeling cared about increases self-confidence and decreases loneliness. If we think we are solving the social anxiety problem discussed in Chapter Four by allowing teens and millennials to "safely" talk to bots because of reduced risk of rejection, we are missing the mark. The latter only serves to perpetuate the problem. Growth occurs when we push the comfort zone a bit. Human relationships, which rely on varying degrees of intimacy and vulnerability, although a little scary, *increase our resilience to stress.* This type of resilience cannot occur if the relationship is with a machine.

If the above doesn't wake you up to what is happening in our current world, perhaps understanding the difference between varying levels of artificial intelligence and their implications can. In his 2017 TEDx Talk, my son explained how, with the current mainstream level of artificial intelligence, we are more vulnerable to hacking, potentially putting us at the mercy of our own robotic weaponry. Indeed, a recent study determined that the Department of Defense was highly hackable.[54] Those who believe in conscious robots argue that if, for example, a foreign government hacks into our robotic weapon system, turning it on our own commercial airplanes as an act of terrorism, our artificially and consciously intelligent system would see that the weapons are being turned on commercial airplanes (holding passengers) and would not allow the operation to proceed. Fair enough. But, how do we instill ethical principles in intelligent robots? We are a complex species, and I don't think it is as simple as training the robot to do what's best for most while creating the least amount of harm (a standard ethical guideline). And, if robots start making many of the major decisions, what happens to our brains? Remember, Allan Schore's research verifies it's the human connection with each other that allows our brains to develop in the first place. Most neuroscientists will tell you that your brain needs just as much exercise as the rest of your body. Use it or lose it or meld it.

That's right. Melding technology with the human brain is on the horizon. The field of medicine is benefiting already from artificial intelligence and advances in technology. Robotic surgery is helping millions. Its precision performance exceeds that of human hands. Nanorobots in medicine help us treat infectious diseases more quickly and accurately and can perform surgeries that repair damaged cells. Without a doubt, this type of intelligence is exciting and fast-moving into our everyday reality, promising longer and healthier lives. That is—if we survive it. Several tech leaders believe that in order to keep up with nanotechnology, we will have to essentially meld the human brain with the machine. Say what? Yes, Elon Musk, for example, has funded a company called Neuralink, which hopes to design and implant nanotechnology into the human brain so that the super intelligent computers we create today don't turn us all into "house cats" as he says.

Musk, along with other leaders in the tech field, believe the human house cat scenario is a definite possibility, and that one of the viable ways around being governed by our own manmade machines, is to increase our brain's intelligence by melding it with the machine. This would decrease the chance of the machine outsmarting us and taking over. The concern is that if artificial intelligence and nanotechnology cross paths for the greater evil (instead of the above examples of it being used for the greater good in medicine), we could have a full-blown catastrophe on our hands. Some muse that artificially intelligent nanotechnology could act like viruses that we ingest without knowing it and wreak havoc on the human race. It seems we've gotten excited about AI without fully examining its dark side and the destruction it could cause, just like with alcohol, cigarettes, atomic energy, and smartphones. So, what do we do?

Voice Your Opinion

When we hold worries inside, we either send ourselves on a never-ending merry-go-round of rumination or we resign ourselves to helplessness. Because artificial intelligence is being developed as I write, policies also need to be made to safeguard us against its dangers. Tech companies, such as Microsoft and Google, should have clear security measures in place before developing super-intelligent beings. Our government needs to fully understand the risks of artificially intelligent weaponry. Write to the policymakers. Let them know your concerns. Remember, doing something about a problem can increase a sense of effectiveness, which decreases anxiety and depression (common stressors).

The Human Revolution

When Ariana Huffington wrote *The Sleep Revolution,* her aim was to infiltrate change in our cultural approach to sleep. She began an educational tour that primarily addressed college students, educating them on the importance of sleep and how to get it. When Susan Cain wrote the book *Quiet* on the support for and understanding of introverts, she followed up with what she now calls the *Quiet Revolution,* which is a "mission to unlock the power of introverts for the benefit of us all." So, why not have a *Human Revolution* in which we could revive the importance of the power of humans over the power of machines? We could gather, educate, and implement programs that maximize human relationships for the better good. Sometimes, we get so enamored with what's ahead, we sacrifice sleep, we miss out on the gifts of introverts, and we fail to notice the power of being with each other without machines.

Please Don't Hire AI Psychotherapists, Babysitters, or Caregivers (As a Start)

Humans need humans, especially when it comes to caregiving and emotional support. Robots, no matter how adept, will never replace that. They'll never have eyes that express the depth of their souls nor an understanding of what it means to suffer. No algorithm will ever fully understand what it means to be human. Humans need to feel cared for—if we don't, we don't thrive. This is the basis of all psychotherapy. It is the genuineness of a compassionate therapeutic

131

relationship that heals, not necessarily the therapist's methodology. If we hire AI therapists or babysitters that understand content—that can tell us how to think or when bedtime is—we will be missing the mark entirely. Remember that love and understanding is the key to our well-being and no robot, no matter how smart, will ever love and truly understand the complexity of your being. People understand people. Robots respond to people. Those are two different things.

7

INFORMATION OVERLOAD

"Constant access to communications, computers and data has changed societal expectations. Immediate responsiveness and continuous productivity are now expected."

—Adam Gazzaley, MD, PhD,
Author of *The Distracted Mind*

information overload *(noun):* exposure to or provision of too much information or data.

A young woman sat down on my couch one morning and said, "I feel overwhelmed by all the bad things happening [in our country]. I think I'm depressed."

"There's been a lot of negativity, which can feel oppressive, but it seems your depression is connected to feeling helpless to do anything about it," I said.

"Well, I can vote, but I can't stop crazy people from shooting up a yoga studio."

(She was referring to a recent tragedy in which a reportedly misogynistic male killed two women and injured four others during a yoga class in an upscale Florida yoga studio. My client, whom I'll call, Jane, practiced yoga routinely.)

"No, but there are things you *could* do."

"I think I need to stop reading the news," she mused.

"Yes, setting boundaries around what you do and don't ingest helps," I replied.

People are angry and despondent these days. Many of my clients, like Jane, feel overwhelmed by the daily bombardment of negative news stories. Because of social media and technology, in general, we get our news fast and in spades. Anytime we open our phones, we risk being pinged with the latest breaking news of a shooting, campaign-slandering, or opioid-death incident. As President Obama said in a 2015 interview with the *Huffington Post's* Sam Stein, "We live in a twenty-four-seven, Twitter-fed, constant news cycle, and everything's a crisis!" He meant that we begin to *think* everything is a crisis. He went on to point out that many times when we thought, "This is it—it's over!" things turned out okay.

"I miss Obama," my client went on to say. As presidents are historically called "the father of our nation," my patient was referring to the fact that she felt less protected these days by our current administration. Often, when we feel stressed, like from information overload or anything else, it can be offset by a secure feeling that someone has our back. As a nation, this person is usually the president. But if there isn't a good father figure at the helm, the anxious searching for soothing, like in our phones and on the internet, increases, leaving us more consumed than free.

The famous psychoanalyst Rollo May once said, "It is an old and ironic habit of human beings to run faster when we have lost our way." This statement couldn't be more apropos to our current culture in the United States. In order to intervene on the stress information overload is causing us as Americans, we must 1) admit we've lost our way and 2) understand how it happened and 3) make changes in our lifestyles to get back on track.

The current political climate of divisiveness, manifesting in anything from the condoning of racism to the debate on gun laws, demonstrates a regression not a progression in American values. The reality we've hurt our planet, given the degree to which climate change is now wreaking havoc via hurricanes, floods, and storms indicates we've lost touch with the earth and all it offers. But, most importantly, *the rising number of Americans who are stressed, anxious, depressed, and killing themselves screams "we've lost our way."* We don't feel potent, and we certainly don't dream big, as anxiety and depression are predicated on impotence and hopelessness.

So, how did this happen? How did we, as Americans, lose our way? How did our lives move from leisurely Sunday drives and picnics with friends to seven-day work weeks and 24/7 digital relationships? How many times in your week have you heard yourself or someone else say, "I'm so overwhelmed" or "I don't have enough hours in the day"?

Given the multitude of ways we may be contacted, we struggle to keep up with the expectations digital communication was supposed to make easy. Heads buried in our devices, we try to respond to the never-ending flow of email and increasingly tight deadlines as companies expect work to be done swiftly and in abundance, and friends and family expect to be responded to within minutes of texting. (I am not immune to this as I admit I've become agitated at times when my son or husband take more than a couple of hours to respond to a text message.)

With handheld computers, it doesn't take much to join a virtual meeting, punch out a document, or respond to a friend. We've come to expect and demand things of one another, fast and in abundance. With Google Calendar, bosses, secretaries, colleagues, family

135

members, and schools can fill our schedules with their priorities. These events are color-coded into our digital agendas, creating a mosaic of "to-dos." We've become so lassoed by these "to-dos" that we forget why it is we're doing them. Unaware of how much time we spend on digital communication and media consumption, we don't notice that we've estranged ourselves from life's deepest meaning— our relationships with each other. We've come to see each other as obstacles. We've come to fear one another's differences. We've come to communicate with each other virtually, believing this is more efficient. We've lost the comfort of a human "holding environment," one where we have each other's backs. Instead, we perseverate on falling short, disappointing, failing, or missing out.

I Can't Stop; I've Got too Much to Do

"There is more to life than increasing its speed."
—Gandhi

Text messages, emails, notifications, instant messages, robocalls, TV news, radio news, and internet news barrage us daily all via our smartphones, tablets, TVs, and laptops. On our way to looking up information, we sometimes have to wade through other information. Drug ads that lure us into wanting the pill that can fix our physical and emotional pain but wind up scaring us with all the dangerous side effects (including death), distract us from our mission. Then, we realize we got sidetracked. What were we doing? Oh, that's right, searching for the YouTube video that will teach us how to get fit with twenty-minute workouts (because time is of the essence, you know). But, first, we decide to check our email, so we don't fall too far behind. Emails arrive in droves, and we'll be flattened by them if we don't keep up. In the midst of checking email, we remember autopay bills are coming out this week. We should check the bank account to make sure we have enough money to cover them. What? Our password expired? All of a sudden, our brains fail us and we have to look up the old password (in that app that is supposed to keep passwords safe) in order to reset the new password. And so, it goes.

Where is the quiet, the place of calm in the mind that allows us to connect with ourselves, each other, and the earth? The space that permits us to tune into our feelings, talk with a friend for more than five minutes, or take a nature walk? That seat is already taken. External information and demands stream into our psyches on an hourly basis, forcing us to continuously process visual, auditory, and verbal stimuli, much of it negative and some of it downright jarring—if we choose to pull out our phones and "check" them or glance at the airport or restaurant television, because TVs are everywhere now.

Let's look at our phone-checking habits for a minute. What I mean by "checking" one's phone is pulling it out of your pocket or purse to look at it. Why do you do this? Maybe you are legitimately waiting for an important message from a potential employer. Or, maybe you're hoping for a text from the new guy you just met. Regardless of what you think you're looking for, you are most likely looking for hope and connection but living with the illusion that you have so much to do you must check your phone, frequently. In fact, the frequency in which you phone check may be the frequency in which you feel unsettled, unsatisfied, or alone. You may not realize the connection between the emotional longing and the frequent phone checking, but it is there.

Well, you *may* be temporarily uplifted when you find the hoped-for email from the potential employer inside the little envelope icon on your phone. You *may* feel instantly happy when you find that the new guy you met did, indeed, text you and wants to go out. It's this kind of intermittent reinforcement that keeps us going back for more. Like the slot machine that occasionally rings a $100 win, sometimes the smartphone bears good news! Knowing that's possible, you keep looking for the win, but really you're just *"running to stand still."* The U2 lyric reminds us of what addiction can feel like, because, like it or not, many of us are addicted to our smartphones.

Device checking stimulates the stress hormone, cortisol, as it calls our immediate attention to a possible stressor. (Remember, both positive and negative events can cause stress.) The smartphone, in particular, can be toxic in this sense. The "ding" alerting us to a text message actually alerts our brains to danger. The "ring" of the phone tells us news of some kind, any kind, is about to intrude on us and we better be prepared. Of course, we're not thinking this consciously, but the "dings," "pings," and "rings" signal our brains to pump out adrenaline so as to prepare for what awaits. Phone checking increases stress and then we unknowingly check the phone to decrease stress.

We work harder, stay up later, run faster in order to "achieve" something. We keep our phones on at night and work beyond healthy capacity in order to "be successful" or stay "connected" by day. We multitask, that's when you "catch up" on the news while simultaneously answering emails and cooking dinner, not realizing that doing so will slow down vs. speed up your reaction time.[55] And, Adam Gazzaley, a neuroscientist and medical doctor, says multitasking is negatively affecting our memories and overall performances on tasks.

In addition to compromises to your cognitive and language performance, there are other reasons to decrease your cell phone use. Desai, Kesari, and Agarwal[56] found that the radiation coming off our cell phones may be damaging our DNA and decreasing fertility in men. Yikes. And, those who talk on their cell phones while driving, even when it's hands-free, are four times more likely to have a car accident. So, the more we try to stay on top of it by attaching ourselves to our phones, the more we may be inhibiting our cognitive abilities, setting ourselves up for oxidative stress which can cause serious health issues and making ourselves vulnerable to automobile accidents. Last, it is mentally taxing to track information so continuously and from so many sources right up until we go to bed. *Mental stress* is also hazardous to our health. Remember, mental and emotional stress can cause increased inflammation in the body, which can create disease.

Still, we are threatened by the belief that if we don't read and answer emails, texts, instant messages, and don't keep up with the news on our drive to work, we could lose our job, lose our friends, and lose touch with the world. Does this sound like a state of generalized anxiety that I described in Chapter Four? Well, it is. I believe information overload is, in part, responsible for the rising rates of anxiety in the US. Since I may have just overloaded you by describing overload, let me suggest one intervention you can try off the bat. It's a place to start before we explore more.

News Detox

As I talk about news detox, I want to reiterate what journalist Laura Ling once said: "One of the single most important freedoms we have is that of an open and free press." She's right, and journalists are to be revered for the work they do. News detox does not insinuate that news journalism isn't valuable or that we shouldn't stay informed. But we need to moderate the input. Remember my friend who was stressed out the day of one of our recent hurricanes? He said he couldn't stop watching the news. Remember the statistics I offered at the beginning of this book on those who qualified for a PTSD diagnosis after chronic news exposure covering the 9/11 terrorist attack? And then there is Jane, who decided she should probably take a break from the news, given its negative affect on her mood. While the news is easily accessible and, frankly, in our faces whether we like it or not, there are concrete ways to reduce news exposure for a set period of time. Listen to music or podcasts in the car instead of the news. Don't turn on the TV news when you come home at night. Don't watch it before bed. Remove notifications and the news apps from your phone. Suspend your newspaper subscription, whether it be hard copy or online. If your habit is to listen to the news while getting ready for work in the morning, change that. Listen to something inspiring. Because of technology, we are more exposed than ever to stress-inducing story after stress-inducing story and can wind up being consumed, if we don't set our own limits.

Stop Texting Me
(But, how do we stay friends?)

"The more helpful our phones get, the harder it is to be ourselves."

—Brian Christian, author of *The Most Human Human:
What Talking with Computers Teaches Us about What It Means to Be Alive*

"I'm calling you because texting everything I want to say is exhausting," my sister says when I answer the phone. She's regularly irritated by her smartphone in that she likes her tech-free time—working in the garden, cooking or listening to a baseball game—but in order to communicate with others, she's found she must text them. She also realizes that as we try to coordinate care for our elderly mother, texting me is the mode of operation that's going to get the most immediate response. I don't like this fact about my current life, which is why I pick up the phone when she calls.

Texting has become the primary method of communication these days, surpassing calling. In fact, texting is the primary use of smartphones in the US;[57] yet, as much as people engage with it, they really don't like it. Daily, clients complain of a friend who confronts them with an issue over text message. Or, they spend oodles of time trying to read between the lines of a message the new person they are dating just sent. They roll their eyes when their phone alerts them to a text in the middle of our session. "Sorry, oh geez, I can't believe he's texting me that, anyway. What were you saying?" Or, "whoops, I forgot to turn that off" only for the phone to ding five minutes later. "What...I thought I turned that off." Is it conscious, unconscious that the smartphone is now a major part of the therapy session? Are clients avoiding the intimacy of therapy, or do they fear missing out on something if they leave the phone in the glovebox? What keeps people tethered to their Messages App?

We feel compelled to check and send messages as it has become the preferred mode of communication, but many of us feel overwhelmed by it at the same time. As a business owner with numerous millennial employees, my husband is so bombarded with text messages that he inevitably misses one or two a day, including mine. This can be disastrous if the person texting is calling in sick to work because "calling in" really means texting these days. My husband stopped calling his employees when they just couldn't seem to check their voicemail. Voicemail...it's practically obsolete for many. Instead, in response to his voice message, he would often get a text: *I saw you called me,* which is code for "text me if you want something because I don't answer my phone or check my voicemail." Even fourteen-year-old Julia from Chapter Six says, "People don't ask me for my phone number because that would be weird." Her generation hardly ever texts as communication primarily happens through Snapchat.

Because talking to one another, even on the phone, feels "weird" these days, we resort to the little keypad on our Messages App even though it is more cumbersome to use than the telephone keypad. Don't say the microphone is easier. You know how much that messes up. One small example is when my friend sent an ex-girlfriend a text that auto-corrected the following sentence from the intended, "I'll keep you abreast," to "I'll keep your breasts." And how many people actually take the time to check and correct their dictated messages? Many are in such a rush, they don't take the time to check and correct. As a result, miscommunications and accidents abound.

Paola, the millennial who withdrew herself from social media for sixteen months, says that so much information was streaming in via text, email, and notifications on her phone that she admits she had gotten into the habit of texting while driving. "I just wanted to get it over with, you know. I'm the kind of person who wants to respond right away so I don't have to deal with it later because there is so much to respond to all the time." This habit resulted in Paola getting into a couple of car accidents. "It was just that split second that I looked down at my phone that caused me to hit the car in front of me." I asked her whether she puts her phone away now that it has caused a couple of car accidents. "I still don't put my phone away when I'm in the car. But, I definitely try to refrain from texting while driving." Why weren't the accidents enough to force Paola to put the phone away? She says she's afraid she'll miss out on something pertinent to making her new online business successful. It's a motivation driven by money as Paola struggles to make it in a city with high rent and expenses and is determined to make this online business fly, which, to her, means always being "on." "I have to keep up, you know. The younger generation is so on top of it (meaning they have social media down, always having lived with it). I don't want to miss out on something that could appeal to them and help my business."

One of the biggest reasons we are held hostage by messaging is that we think texting is safer than talking. After my husband found no success with voicemails, he called a meeting to address his preferred mode of communication. Things improved some, but not entirely. People are stuck in a habit because talking has become anxiety-provoking. With texting, you can avoid answering questions. You can lie a little and not feel so badly. You don't have to risk upsetting someone or looking foolish because you can polish the words and hide behind the screen.

But, hasn't this gone too far? When people end relationships over Snapchat or quit their jobs via text message, we've lost our way. When a client in her fifties asks me if she should discuss her hurt feelings with their boyfriend in person or just text it, we've lost our way. The true self is the part of the self that isn't afraid of looking foolish. It's the wiser self—the calm one. We know when we talk with people, we can stumble, we can get red in the face, we can put our foot in our mouth. That's uncomfortable at best and scary at worst. We live in a highly self-conscious culture—one that can photoshop away blemishes and carefully choose words so as not to stutter. It's a culture that perceives flaws as embarrassing. With texting, we can present ourselves as unfettered. But just like the photoshopped photo, it's not real and it doesn't foster secure attachments. It's not the true self.

Not only do people *not* want to be vulnerable face to face, they don't want to push others away by making *them* feel vulnerable. My clients are just as aware of their own vulnerability as they are of the perceived skittishness of others. Some fear face-to-face or even voice-to-voice communication will put others "on the spot," and they don't want to make them uncomfortable. If we think that telling

143

someone in person how we feel will push him or her away, we have a problem, Captain. Hear me on this: *the only way to form secure attachment is to truly see one another, and the only way to do this is by being our true selves in each other's presence.* Consider the South African greeting, "Sawubonna." It means, "I see you deeply."

Texting gives people the illusion they have more control, but, in fact, relying primarily on text communication deprives people of the confidence to handle the various nuances and emotions that the human condition renders. If there is a conflict via text message, a person doesn't have to respond, but, if there is a conflict in person, the likelihood you'll feel your way through, and grow from it, is higher. We absolutely need to stumble, fall, and repair when building relationships with others. Remember how important this process is in developing secure attachment (see Chapter Two)? Texting protects us from having to find our way in conversations with others, protects us from vulnerability, the discomfort of conflict, and the effort toward resolution. But in actuality, texting as the primary form of communication sets us up for social anxiety. By hiding behind the Messages App, we don't learn the aforementioned social skills needed to be with one another. Blind people may not be able to see facial expressions, but they are keenly aware of fluctuation in tone and the vibration of bodily presence. An automated voice, translating a text message from a lover, or a heart emoji placed next to "thinking of you" is not going to help us develop the social skills needed for lasting connection and intimacy. And, remember, *intimacy helps create secure attachment, and secure attachment helps us handle stress.*

Reducing the Stress of Texts

Call More

You can make the excuse that texting is safer than talking on one's cell phone as I just discussed the hazards of cell phone radiation. But we both know that using earbuds or putting someone on speaker can solve that. But sometimes you may not want others to hear your intimate conversation, or you may just want to respect others' space when in public. I still say that if you want to create secure attachment or, in other words, healthier and more rewarding relationships, even with coworkers, bosses, and teachers, then calling (at least half the time) will help you do this. Sure, texting can be more convenient in the above situations and may be better than not communicating at all, but if you have the opportunity to not disturb the peace by calling your date, your supervisor, or your mother (for that matter), do it. Remember, every time you text instead of call, you run the risk of becoming a little more socially awkward.

Write a Letter Once in a While

When is the last time you did this? I don't mean writing a letter via email (although, that's the next best thing), I mean writing a handwritten card or letter. When my kids get and give gifts, they address or thank the person with a handwritten note. My husband and I helped them develop the habit when they were young. Some of the most beautiful words my sons have ever expressed have been via these notes. They've touched me and others profoundly. When you see someone's handwriting, it brings you closer to his humanness, his realness. When I say sending an email is the next best thing, what I mean is that it still allows the writer to express himself more fully but lacks the personal quality of the handwriting. Don't you become intrigued when you get a handwritten card or letter in your mailbox (the one attached to your apartment or house?) It feels good. It kind of slows everything down as you take the time to open the envelope and read the words someone wrote in her personal handwriting style. When my mother, at the age of nineteen, had a writing relationship with a man fighting overseas in World War II, he told her that the pink stationery she used warmed his heart. It smelled of her perfume and felt like her. Neither email nor text messaging allows for these elements of communication. Perhaps you can make a point of writing someone a card or letter this week. Notice how you feel when doing it. It may relieve you a bit from feeling overwhelmed.

Stop Calling Me
(The Era of Robocalls)

"Everybody is annoyed by robocalls; hatred of them might be the only thing that everyone in America agrees on."

—John Oliver

At the time of writing this, robocalls (those automated callers that ask you to buy something, warn you about something or speak in a language you don't understand) take up about 30 percent of all our incoming calls. First Orion, a provider of phone call transparency solutions, predicts that this year (2019) that number will soar to nearly 50 percent. Perhaps you've already noticed this. In fact, 60 percent of all complaints made to the Federal Communications Commission are about robocalls. They're disruptive, relentless, and exhausting, and many of them are illegal. It's akin to harassment as people are receiving calls falsely claiming they are being investigated by the IRS, or that there is an arrest in their name. By now, most people know not to believe these scams, but there are some, mostly the elderly, who get alarmed and for whom they cause more than just annoyance, but substantial distress.

Robocalls are enough to make people not want to answer their phones anymore and, thus, defeats the purpose of my encouragement that you do in the previous section. Yes, the Do Not Call Registry may help a bit, but, really, they just block sales calls from non-scammers. Your cell phone or landline carrier can help somewhat in that they try to determine which calls are robocalls and block them before they get to you, but many will charge you for the super-duper blocking, which is supposed to be more effective. You can also get call-blocking apps, such as Robokiller. Sounds daunting but they reduce the robocall deluge to a further degree. Protecting yourself from the shadow side of technology comes at a price these days. New fake telephone numbers are being created constantly and, so, regardless of protections you may have set up to block these calls, you'll inevitably still get some that haven't been flagged as robo.

But, I'm not here to talk about the technical response to robocalling—you can discuss that with your carrier, the Federal Communications Commission (FCC), or the Do Not Call Registry. My concern is how robocalling is contributing to the stress you feel from having too much to manage. It's one more thing, one more "ring" that sets off a stress response, one more minute of your day trying to move an obstacle. Robocalling also unconsciously contributes to the psychological dis-ease that we can't trust our own technology, let alone each other. If, several times throughout the day, you are alerted to the fact that someone is trying to get something from you, it sets off your alarm bells, causes you to be more vigilant, and makes you feel a little less trusting. It seems everywhere we turn we must watch out for being hacked. Our privacy is disappearing, and so is our control over our personal technology. The field of cybersecurity is burgeoning in the US, and if we think about it too much, it all feels a bit surreal. Big brother has descended, and this leaves Americans uncertain and anxious.

Teens are warned that anything they text could be held against them. Teachers and administrators remind them to be careful about what they post as colleges are watching. When you surf online, Google ads spring up appealing to your personal interest because

Google pays attention to what you search. Yet, every day, most of us text, post, search, and get invaded by spam and scam. Robocalls are just another straw on the camel's back but seem to rile people more than the other forms of invasion I just mentioned. John Oliver just ranted on his show about robocalls, threatening to robocall the FCC. Once again, our access to live conversation is being hindered by an invasive phenomenon that is emblematic of our time. *As stress in the US goes up, connections with each other go down.* I encourage you to not let robocalls get in the way of using your phone to talk to people. My solutions may not stop the calls, but pay attention as they can alleviate your perpetual feeling of overwhelm and help to dissipate the frustration you feel from call invasion. Here are two interventions you can try.

Dealing with Robocalls

Silence the phone. Remember how the ring of the phone triggers a physiological stress response in the body? While it's not practical to silence your phone, in that you'll miss some calls from people you may actually want to talk to, it can help to reduce the number of times your body jumps into vigilant mode because of the number of robocalls that set off your ringer. Because robocalls are increasing at expediential rates, silencing can be a short-term but immediate option to reducing stress. And you don't have to do it for the entire day—a few hours without rings can give you a needed break.

Learn to meditate. There are myriad apps out there and plenty of teachers who can teach you to meditate. It doesn't have to take a lot of time, and it can help you immensely with information overload and daily annoyances, including robocalls. Here's why. When we meditate, we focus our attention on a simple point of reference—our breathing, for example. However, we also widen our field of attention to include an awareness of everything around us. While the breathing centers us, the awareness expands. Awareness doesn't mean that we react to what enters our field of attention. For example, when my dog barks while I'm meditating, I don't shoosh him. I'm aware of the barking while focusing my attention on the breath. Meditation is a practice in non-reactivity with keen awareness. Of course, I'm going to react if my husband yells for help because he's cut his finger, but I don't need to react to the barking dog. Meditation trains us to attend to what we absolutely need to attend to. In this way, it can help us be aware of the phone ringing or of the anonymous phone number and, yet, not react to it by physically picking it up or by shouting expletives at the robocaller. This kind of awareness without reactivity will help offset the stress the calls cause in the first place.

Can I Take a Vacation?
(How to Do So on a Daily Basis)

"Vacation can make you more productive—just ask the Europeans."
—Elizabeth Schulze, reporter CNBC

Compared to most countries in the world, Americans are not big on vacation time. The average employee gets a whopping two weeks per year, but many Americans aren't paid for a single day off. In contrast, many European countries get four-to-eight weeks paid vacation with Austria topping the list at a total of thirty-five paid days off per year! Apparently, Americans work even more than the notoriously overworked Japanese—137 hours more per year to be exact—and most of us feel it. Look around. Many of us living in the United States never really leave our jobs these days. Both employer expectation and availability via our smartphones, laptops, and tablets are partially responsible for this.

In addition, we seem to do personal business while at work and, then work during what was supposed to be our personal time. In other words, with technology and the constant access to information, we may be multitasking too much and not using our time efficiently. I spoke with the vice president of human resources for a large Silicon Valley tech company who stated: "Personal life and work have become so blurred, that they are hard to separate out...there is a lot of shopping, web-surfing and personal emailing that occurs during working hours, making many employees *feel* like they work more than they do." Web-surfing while on the job is what I call stealing time. I'm not knocking those who do it. We need a break. But, because we don't take true breaks by stepping away from the office (the computer, the phone), we don't get the rejuvenation we need to work effectively. As a result, we *steal* breaks by switching screens while at our desks or by taking calls from our spouses. Because this is stealing time instead of intentionally taking time, these kinds of breaks aren't fulfilling. What's more, they lead to having to be "on" when we're supposed to be "off"—working after hours to catch up on what we didn't get done earlier in the day.

Attorneys are particularly known for being available during what are supposed to be their "off" hours. I remember our attorney telling my husband and me that we could certainly text her if we needed anything while she vacationed in the Greek Islands. *Uh, no.* "Nothing is so urgent as to bug you on your vacation." But, that is what many Americans do these days, and it is what many employers expect. My clients in the corporate world are always available while on vacation, and many of them spend several hours a day working when they're supposed to be snoozing, snorkeling, or powering down. Why? Some are afraid they will lose their job if they don't keep up with the demands. Others fear that if they offload work to a colleague, it will be evident they are replaceable. So, they work on vacation. That's not a vacation.

Much like what Paola was saying about not wanting to miss a beat so she can make her online business a success, some US residents are chasing the American Dream and are afraid of not excelling if they don't stay plugged in. This is especially true for the self-employed. When you run your own business, there is always something you could be doing to increase or maintain its success. But being constantly "on" can make multitasking a way of life. As a result, tasks get drawn out and left hanging because of how frequently they are interrupted. And, taking time away from the job can feel threatening, like we're losing an opportunity by doing so. I see the same phenomenon among students who do their homework on their tablets or laptops. They screen switch and what may have been a one-hour assignment can drag out for three or four hours.

Then there are the communal workspaces. This latest fad was designed with the idea that employees could collaborate more and be less isolated. But it didn't take into consideration one huge distraction: noise. Studies have shown that intermittent noise is more distracting than constant noise. So, if an employee is trying to concentrate on writing a document and hears intermittent conversation occurring between her coworkers, she is more likely to get distracted and take longer to finish the task. Furthermore, introverts get hit hard when they are placed in communal work settings. They are much more affected by noise than extroverts and, therefore, can experience a drop in productivity, which only serves to increase stress. Then you have the social aspect. While companies may have made people feel less isolated, they've also tempted them with socializing while on the job, pushing their workday into evening hours, which creates that phenomenon of always feeling "on."

The problem with low or no vacation time, the fear of missing out (FOMO), and noise distraction/interruption is that our bodies never really get a chance to recharge, nor do we have the space in our minds to notice a world beyond work. We, as Americans, are defined by our work. Go to a party and the most common question will be, "So, what do you do [for a living]?" Our noses in our phones, responding to text messages while driving, checking email while vacationing, and listening to the news while eating breakfast, we inundate ourselves with information overload and refuse to take a vacation from it for fear we'll fall behind. Fear equals the presence of danger, imagined or not, and danger sets off our stress response. This is a constant state for many Americans—the fear of falling behind— which means we're in some form of perpetual stress.

So, how do we take a vacation when 1) we don't get the vacation time to take or 2) we think taking it will jeopardize our success and 3) the workplace setting is inefficient, rendering the need for us to work beyond normal business hours? First, not having any paid days off is a tough position to be in. With a shrunken middle class and continued emphasis on feeding the rich vs. the poor (think tax cuts and wage inequality), we leave our hourly wage workers without pensions or health insurance. Many Americans are struggling financially. Vacation to hourly employees seems like a thing of rom coms or something wealthy people do. Some work two or three jobs to put their kids through college, pay off medical bills, or simply feed their families. Even if one job gave them a paid day off, it is likely the other would not.

In the case of financial hardship, a blurry work-life balance, or FOMO, it is vitally important to learn how to take "mini-vacations" throughout one's day or week. A mini-vacation is a small amount of time, anywhere from five minutes to five hours, during which we take a break from the task at hand and engage in something non-work related and rejuvenating. Those are the key words: *non-work related and rejuvenating.* Researcher Adam Gazzaley, PhD, says that we usually only keep our attention on a task for about eleven minutes before switching to something else. In addition, workers are being interrupted every three minutes these days (because of the culprits of information overload such as the smartphone, communal workspaces, and our own distracted brains), costing hundreds of billions of dollars in decreased productivity. So, if task-switching or multitasking is already proving to decrease productivity, why not take a true break from a task in order to rejuvenate and recharge your batteries so that when you return to it, you return with a calmer and more focused mind? Here are some ideas about how to do that.

Change Your Environment

We get so mired in what we are doing and so cooped up in little cubicles or offices that we can become a permanent fixture of our own environments. Not only do people forget to get up from their chairs and stretch, but we forget to leave the work environment altogether. This is vital whether you spend most of the day in a quiet office (like I do) or in a communal workspace. Changing the environment can be done by going outside and getting some vitamin D from the sun. It can be done by going to the lobby and sitting for a bit. It can be done by walking the stairwell to get exercise. The farther you can remove yourself, the better. I remember interning at a psychiatric hospital in Southern California. I worked on locked wards and the fences surrounding the place could make you feel as if there were no checking out. The patients were sad, confused, and heavily medicated. I wanted to make a difference in their prognosis and often worked without a break. But after a month or so, I realized I had to get off the hospital grounds once a day. I began to take a lunch break at a small, nearby park that had nothing but two benches

153

and a tiny patch of grass. This little, outdoor space gave me the room to take in the sun, breathe fresh air, and rejuvenate so I could return to the hospital with a bit less stress. Changing my environment gave me a mini-vacation from the intensity of the ward and from the work itself. If you can't get off-site like I did, at least get out of your workspace, even if it means walking down the hall and back. Changing your environment, even for a brief moment, can give you a reprieve from information overload.

Take an Internal Break

Another great option for a mini-vacation while at work is to simply close your eyes and focus on something positive. Rick Hanson, PhD, author of *Hardwiring Happiness*, emphasizes the gain we get from intentionally thinking about and soaking in a positive thought or moment. We have to be intentional about it—that is, to pause and say, "What's good right now?" Because our brains naturally are wired to look for what's wrong or what is missing, this pause is essential. The something positive could be envisioning the smile on your daughter's face or the warmth of a cup of tea in your hands or the smell of the flowers on your desk. It doesn't have to be a monumental thing. There are positives all around us. The fact that you're breathing is a positive. The fact that you have a job is a positive. Taking five minutes to think of something positive and dwelling on it long enough to let it bring a smile to your face, will calm your nervous system and give you that bit of rejuvenation needed to continue with your workday.

If you're at a loss to think of something positive, you can still take that minute or two to engage in mindful breathing. Remember the exercise in Chapter Four? Focusing on your breathing and slowing it down calms the nervous system. Whether you're focusing on something positive or neutrally following your breath, you can do

154

these two things multiple times a day without ever leaving your desk. This can help build a more secure attachment to yourself as you take the time to tend to you.

Take a Staycation

When you need more than a few minutes' break but don't have the financial means, take a true, multi-day staycation. A true staycation means you act as if you are on vacation but without the expense of having to buy airfare or hotel stays. In order for your staycation to be as relaxed as possible, have your mail held (you wouldn't ordinarily see your mail if you were on a vacation), silence your phone (so as not to get caught up in responding to work demands or menial life demands), and do things in your town or city that you wouldn't ordinarily do—such as exploring a new place to picnic or going out to breakfast or spending a weekday afternoon at the movies. Staycations don't need to cost much, but they can give you a break from the day-to-day grind. The key is to 1) exist as though you are offline by not getting online, answering the phone, or going through the mail. You may even want to refrain from cleaning the house or doing laundry as you wouldn't be doing those things on vacation. You may want to eat out, so you don't have dishes. 2) Do novel activities. Vacations are rejuvenating, in part, because they are a change of scenery and because we often do things we don't ordinarily do in our everyday lives. Since you aren't leaving town on a staycation, get out to new places, walk or take the bus instead of drive, change how you move through your day. Novelty can bring a spark to a burnt-out mind and body.

Lobby for More Vacation Time at Your Place of Work

Because there is no law in the United States that says an employer must grant their workers paid time off, you may have to ask for it.

You may or may not be the type that likes to speak out about change, but if you think your company or organization is not giving any or much paid time off, say something about it. You can do this in a multitude of ways. You can discuss your ideas with other employees and bring up your thoughts in a meeting. You can write to your human resources department. You can talk to your boss. Think about other countries that have twenty, thirty, or more days off. It's the norm. You aren't asking for the moon by asking for more paid days off. You are asking for your sanity. The more US residents speak up about this, the more likely it is that we can change our workaholic lifestyle.

The Gist of Dealing with Information Overload

Set Boundaries. Boundaries are a key concept in attachment theory. While the word "boundaries" may have been overused in recent decades, its meaning is more applicable today than ever before. If we want to control the deluge of news and information, we need to set boundaries around it. This means being intentional about where you go to dinner or, if you're in a restaurant with a TV, sitting in an area where you can't see the screen. Really. If you can't turn off the TV attached to your cardio machine, throw your towel over it and turn on some tunes—or, hey, talk to the person on the equipment next to you. At airports, face the windows if possible, close your eyes, and meditate (yep) or read a nondigital book. At home, reduce the visibility of screens by removing them from certain rooms or covering them in a cabinet.

Turn off your devices entirely for substantial periods of the day so you are not tempted to google the news or other supposed interests that lead you astray. I know you may be wondering why you would google the news when you're trying not to watch it, but FOMO (fear of missing out) is a strong component of American culture. In addition, turning off news apps and notifications on your devices will reduce information overload. Whether it's a national broadcast of the latest school shooting or your friend, gushing over her new baby on Facebook when you just had a miscarriage, if you don't see it, it won't bombard you. Sometimes, people turn to the device unconsciously, looking for connection. Trust me, if you want to connect to people, turning off notifications won't prevent that from happening.

Set boundaries with people. If colleagues or family members constantly bring up the news and you are trying to set boundaries around it, let them know you don't want to discuss the news at that moment. Change the subject to something that makes you feel good, calm, happy, or take a break from the conversation altogether.

In order to set these boundaries, you may need to *change your routine*. If your habit is to come home and turn on the TV, scroll through your phone, or work some more on your laptop, do something else. Turn on some music you like. Go for a walk without your phone, play with the dog, call a friend, read a book. It may feel strange or even lonely to be without a vehicle for information streaming as we've come to believe these devices—be they TVs, computers or smartphones—are the way to stay connected. But, as I discussed in my chapter on loneliness, addressing loneliness means learning to be *with* ourselves.

Boundaries are lines we draw to provide ourselves with necessary containment. Just like the comforting embrace of a parent's arms around an overwhelmed child, boundaries help protect us from invasive and harmful stimuli that can otherwise adversely impact our nervous systems. The embrace calms and centers us, so can the boundaries. Imagine them as protective arms around yourself rather than steel walls that shut others out.

8

How Sleep Became an American Problem

"Today, the problem of too little sleep, and the quest for more of it, is as acute as ever."
—Consumer Reports, 2016

Are We Sleep-Deprived or Unrested?

"When we shrink our whole reality down to pending projects, when our life becomes our endless to-do list, it's difficult to put them aside each night and let ourselves fall asleep and connect with something deeper."

—Arianna Huffington, author of *The Sleep Revolution*

sleep *(noun)*: the natural, easily reversible, periodic state of many living things that is marked by the absence of wakefulness, the loss of consciousness of one's surroundings and is considered essential to the restoration and recovery of vital bodily and mental functions.

It was post 9/11 and day number four of not sleeping. At least, I didn't think I had slept, but, by that point, time was elusive. It had been a full week of seeing clients, of managing my tenacious and tireless preschooler, my teething new baby, laundry, groceries, and intermittent news stories about the war in Iraq. It was now Thursday evening. I was in a partial version of the clothes I'd worn to bed the night before. My four-year-old was begging me to get the toy man's hands exactly on the toy truck's steering wheel or he was going to have a meltdown, and my six-month-old was crying. Or was he? I looked over and remembered I'd put him in the swing. Ironically, he was peacefully drifting into the unconscious. I had hallucinated the cry. The effects of my insomnia had gone too far.

Why are so many Americans suffering from sleeplessness in the twenty-first century? The number of people in the United States who sleep less than six hours per night grew by 15 percent between 2013 and 2017.[58] It grew despite the numerous options for sleep medicines on the market. Will it continue to grow, despite the increasing popularity of practiced "sleep hygiene" and despite the frequently publicized associated hazards of sleep deprivation on our overall health? It seems our pressure to produce and our need to be connected with technology may be affecting our sleep, both directly and indirectly. Some research indicates our diet, work schedules, and a culture that associates getting little sleep with being "tough" also contribute to sleep deprivation in our country.

Let's face it; our society has changed since the nine-hour-a-night lifestyle of the 1940s. Its increasing demands are affecting our sleep. From longer work hours to the buzzing of text messages at night to the blue light from our e-readers, intrusions into our sleep are growing. The repercussions of such facts are disturbing, and they don't just affect adults. In 2004, the National Sleep Foundation reported that 30 percent of our children were getting less than adequate sleep. Then, in 2006, this same foundation reported that nearly 50 percent of our nation's adolescents were sleep-deprived. Mine are two of them.

The latest report from the CDC indicates that approximately 35 percent of adult Americans sleep six hours or less per night. But, some researchers wonder whether we truly have an epidemic on our hands or not. They say that the burgeoning of sleep medicine and sleep advertising has Americans misinformed about sleep loss.[59,60] Others will tell you that short sleep duration is a growing and dangerous phenomenon in the United States....one that negatively affects our emotional, cognitive, and physical health and one that can even be lethal.[61,62]

Let's look at some CDC statistics. Apparently, the Southeastern states of the US are getting the least amount of sleep. Interestingly, they are also the geographic area with the worst rates of obesity, diabetes, and heart disease (conditions that lack of sleep seem to exacerbate.) Women have more trouble sleeping than men (maybe because of hormonal changes that can affect sleep or because of other factors such as juggling children, work and home that seem to fall on women more than men). Middle-aged people sleep less than younger or older adults (perhaps because of middle-aged responsibilities). Ethnic minorities sleep less than whites (probably an economic factor). And, sedentary people sleep less than active people (exercise helps one sleep).

Despite these statistics, a question I wrestle with is whether our *sleep duration* is suffering or whether our *sleep quality* is suffering—and which is worse. Michael Irwin, MD, and his team out of UCLA studied just that. After analyzing seventy-two sleep studies, they found that if people sleep less than seven hours a night, they tend to have a slight elevation in the biological inflammatory marker, C-Reactive Protein. Because bodily inflammation is responsible for diseases such as diabetes, rheumatoid arthritis, and cardiovascular issues and marked by an elevation in this protein, this finding was significant.

But Irwin discovered something even more fascinating. Sleep *disturbance* (which occurs with insomnia when we sleep lightly, wake up frequently, have trouble falling asleep and/or feel unrested) is associated with *two* inflammatory markers: elevations in CRP *and* Interleukin-6. Not only were these markers more evident in the sleep disturbed groups than in the short duration groups, their statistical significance was higher.

Why the difference between sleep disturbance (also known as sleep fragmentation) and sleep duration less than seven hours? Well, if sleeper #1 is sleeping a solid but short duration of six and a half hours a night, he may be benefiting from the full ninety-minute sleep cycles that allow him to dream and achieve deep sleep, therefore decreasing the chances that his body is being adversely affected by the mere six and half hours of slumber. If sleeper #2 is sleeping eight hours, but it is a fitful sleep—she wakes easily and frequently and feels unrested the next day—she may not be getting the kind of deep sleep needed to restore the body and brain for optimal functioning.

Is sleep fragmentation the greater of the two evils because it is the result of stress?

I know that in my own life if my husband asks how many hours of sleep I got the night before, unless it is an extremely low number, the question seems somewhat irrelevant. What matters to me is if I slept *well* not long. This notion is supported by Jerry Siegel's research with hunter-gatherer populations of Bolivia, Namibia, and Tanzania. Across these three groups, there seemed to be an average sleep duration of six and a half hours per night with no middle-of-the-night awakenings of any significance. These groups were deemed generally healthy and didn't suffer from many of the chronic diseases modern Americans do, like diabetes, cardiovascular disease or autoimmune disease.[63] It's noteworthy that the hunter-gatherers aren't exposed to the *chronic* stressors most American's face in daily urban (or even rural) life, such as work stress, economic stress, and information overload.

Another way to look at this is to understand the impact of *stress* on the body's inflammatory markers. There has been plentiful research on the fact that stress-related anxiety and depressive disorders are associated with an elevation in C-Reactive Protein.[64] What's more, research shows that prolonged stress in general affects cortisol production, which when out of whack, inhibits the body's ability to regulate inflammation. The result: stress can cause mental or physical illness via unregulated inflammation in the body.

It is very possible that what we thought was a cause and effect relationship between little sleep and disease is really a relationship between psychological stress and disease, with sleep disturbance as a symptom that goes with the territory. In other words, people who struggle with sleep are generally more stressed, and this overall stress, whether experienced during the day or at night, may be the more significant factor in increasing inflammatory markers. I'm not saying that sleep loss isn't a big deal. I can tell you firsthand that it is. What I am saying is that treating our stress levels may be just, if not more, crucial than going after sleep disturbance first. In other words, you may want to emphasize vacation and meditation and worry less about that Ambien refill.

But, what about the people who don't have sleep disorders but intentionally don't sleep much because they don't feel they have the time for it? Working late into the night or getting up at the crack of dawn for that early phone meeting is more common than ever among my clients, not just in the corporate world, but in the academic world, the legal world, the medical field, and so on. The complaint often goes something like this: "I have to stay up late because I won't get things done otherwise. And I have to get up early to stay on top of everything."

What many Americans don't realize is that we are more efficient—we think better, perform better, do better academically and

163

athletically—when we get sleep. It seems we sometimes burn the candle at both ends because we don't use time efficiently. We're distracted by our devices, tired, and, therefore, not as focused as we could be on the tasks at hand. We are resentful of the workload, so we steal time with unfulfilling activities such as watching YouTube videos, surfing social media sites, shopping online, or overeating. But, the distraction, fatigue, and avoidance only serve to elongate the time it takes to fulfill work and academic obligations.

We also live in a culture that promotes "achievement." We equate fame and fortune with *being somebody*. Many believe that if they take the time to sleep, they won't get anywhere in life. One millennial said to me, "How am I supposed to make partner [in my legal firm] if I don't sacrifice sleep?" That is the dilemma many Americans feel they're in as they are governed by the carrot of gaining importance through career success. *Maybe the problem lies in why we think we're not important in the first place.*

Creating a Secure Attachment to Yourself

If you want to worry less, feel more connected, and be in the driver's seat of your life, learning how to acknowledge your importance, no matter what, is vital. Knowing you're important *outside your achievements* is central to establishing a secure attachment to the self. As illustrated in Chapter Seven, it is easy to lose your way, to be run by cultural norms or expectations that actually don't serve your well-being. Making sure you are kind to yourself, compassionate with yourself, and curious about your values, is paramount to living a more rested life.

Often, when people are struggling to sleep at night, it's because they feel helpless to affect a situation that is worrying them. *Focused on the worrisome situation, they fail to recognize how they are suffering right there in their bed, in that moment.* If you are cringing about something you said earlier in the day or criticizing your ability to handle an upcoming event, turn your attention from the object of worry to the worrying self. In other words, instead of trying to problem-solve the past or future situation you're anxious about, recognize with compassion your struggle, your tense body, your racing mind, your fear *in that moment.*

One way to take the flashlight off the object of worry and direct it to the worrying self is to talk to yourself compassionately. Self-compassion is a potent stress-reducer. For example, instead of "I'm so exhausted and worried about money," say, "Judy, I see you're suffering right now. Your mind is tired and needs a break." Compassion is not self-pity. It is understanding.

Research also shows that when we address ourselves by name, in non-first-person pronouns, we have less anxiety, are more able to regulate emotion, and are apt to see future events as more challenging (in a good way) than threatening.[65] For example, instead of saying, "I'm so stressed. I'm going to make mistakes in my presentation tomorrow," try this: "Meg is giving a presentation tomorrow and is worried she'll make mistakes, but mistakes are a normal part of life." Using your name in this way is called *self-distancing.* It creates distance from the stressor and decreases your anxiety about the upcoming event. Self-distancing is not avoidance. It is self-regulating.

Judgment, whether coming from yourself or from others, whether perceived or real, often fuels worry (or fear). Fear can dictate whether someone sacrifices sleep intentionally or simply can't sleep peacefully. For example, if a student says to himself, "well, you dug your own grave by not paying attention in class," he punishes himself and, therefore, has more of likelihood to feel unsafe in his own mind. Furthermore, if he says, "you better get an A in the class," he *threatens* himself to do well, which is stressful. Or, if someone lies awake at night worrying about a life decision, it's usually because she's afraid of making the "wrong" decision. When you assume you are wrong if you choose a particular path, judgment is at play. So how do you suspend judgment?

Suspending judgment is not "letting yourself off the hook." It's not getting hooked (and therefore, stressed) by criticisms and threats in the first place. You can release judgment through mindfulness training. *Observe* your thoughts instead of letting them yank you around. In other words, *watch* your mind. What are you thinking at night before you go to sleep? Are you threatening yourself that you'll be a loser if you don't pass Chemistry? Are you criticizing yourself for saying something "stupid" to a colleague that day? If you don't get tossed around by all the internal should'ves, would'ves, could'ves, you are freer to see what is really there. By getting out of fear and into observation, you get to know *your* values, *your* desires instead of trying to sort through what you think other people want you to do. The true self isn't worried about image. It is quiet, wise, and the anchor to a secure attachment to the self.

Is Sleep Loss Really That Bad for Us?

"Sleep deprivation is the most common brain impairment."

—William C. Dement
Founder of the Sleep Research Center
Stanford University

If we are sleeping so few hours or just poorly, if we have elevations in those inflammatory markers, is it really bad for us? Carol Everson, PhD of the Medical College of Wisconsin, would say yes. She has conducted some impressive studies that document the cost of sleep restriction physically, and the results are sobering. Let me tell you about them—but bear with me as I delve into the science of sleep loss first. In one of Everson's more recent studies, she looked at leukocytes (white blood cells that help counteract disease) in rats as the leukocytes in rats are similar to human leukocytes. What she found was that after ten days of sleep deprivation there was measurable cell stress and subsequent cell damage in the liver, lung, and small intestine marking a 30 percent decrease in antioxidants in the liver alone (a decrease greater than 50 percent is lethal.) While undisturbed recovery sleep of two days produced a marked increase in antioxidants, resetting the liver and lung back to normal, the small intestine did not entirely recover.[66]

From this study, it was clear that sleep deprivation injures cells, creating a pro-inflammatory state and DNA damage. Furthermore, Everson noted that with recovery sleep, cells were being produced en masse in the small intestine as they tried to repair the damage done during sleep deprivation. This created a metabolic burden on the organs. So, in their effort to recover lost sleep, this new cellular production was causing damage.

Did you know that lack of sleep can also affect our bones and contribute to diseases like osteoporosis? Another study on rats, conducted by Carol Everson's team, found that chronically inadequate sleep (in this case seventy-two days of short sleep duration—the equivalent of 10–12 percent of a rat's lifetime) rendered low amounts of new bone formation and increased bone resorption (the combination of which is indicative of osteopenia— the forerunner to osteoporosis). The bone in these sleep-restricted rats was compared to a control group and showed that bone metabolism and bone marrow composition suffered as a result of the seventy-two days of restricted sleep.[67] It appears sleep might be just as important as calcium intake when considering the health of our bones.

What is particularly noteworthy about Everson's conclusions is that a routine doctor's visit would not detect this kind of damage, as it wouldn't necessarily show up on blood tests, making sleep deprivation a "silent killer," as she calls it. This may sound dramatic, but we can't deny the science that has come out of Everson's lab and many others. Research indicates that sleep deprivation adversely affects our neural oscillations that inform cognitive functioning.[68,69] Specifically, it seems that attention, learning and working memory suffer as a result of sleep loss.[70] What's more, is that decision-making, which relies on emotional processing, is even more affected by sleep deprivation than other cognitive tasks.

So, lack of sleep or lack of restorative sleep can cause cognitive impairment (to the point where driving a car when severely sleep-deprived has the equivalent effect as driving drunk),[71] it affects our ability to focus on tasks, remember things, learn things, and it messes with our better judgment. But if you think you can jumpstart your sleep-deprived self with a shot or two of java, think again. According to WD Kilgore from Harvard Medical School, the use of stimulants, such as caffeine, after sleep loss does *not* improve decision-making.[72]

The latter is particularly important for teachers and parents to understand. What may be deemed "bad behavior" in a child could actually be the result of poor sleep impacting his or her his ability to regulate emotion and impulses. In other words, kids and adolescents who, for whatever reason, aren't getting restorative sleep can be adversely, neurologically affected. Studies show that sleep-deprived adolescents are more irritable, more reward-seeking (think video games, drugs, and alcohol, and other instant gratifiers), have greater reactivity to noise and exaggerated responses to peer acceptance and rejection.[73,74,75]

Here lies another potential vicious cycle in which kids, who are exposed to multiple stressors today, sleep less as a result. Their sleep loss then causes off-putting behavior as they try to navigate the world of school, peers, and identity—behavior they are often punished for. We need to be thoughtful about how we, as adults, respond to adolescent behavior. While adolescents need boundaries, they also deserve our help and understanding. After all, 73 percent of Generation Z say they aren't getting enough emotional support these days.

Looking back on my insomniac years, it now makes sense that my autoimmune disease, which had been in remission for thirteen years, flared up. Repeated episodes of joint inflammation began to occur after five chronic years of sleep struggle. I believe I couldn't sleep for three reasons: 1) I was overworked, 2) I felt self-induced pressure to parent superbly, given my knowledge as a psychologist, and often felt I was failing at the very thing I imagined nailing, and 3) I was stressed by news stories about global warming and the rise in mass shootings that would subject my kids to more lockdowns in their elementary school life than I had earthquake drills growing up in California.

My stress caused my sleep disturbance which caused further stress on both my body and mind. So, if stress is a major factor in sleep deprivation, let's look at what stressors we can control to improve sleep.

Relationships to Improve Sleep, No Kidding!

"I think the most common cause of insomnia is simple: it's loneliness."

—Heath Ledger

We know relationships with each other are the key to understanding attachment theory, but what does attachment theory have to do with sleep? A child's attachment experience informs his or her adult experience of close relationships. I'm sure you know people who are constantly wondering where their boyfriend is, why he isn't calling, who can't stop talking or thinking about him until he finally makes contact. I'm sure you know others who tend to pull away when you try to hug them or resist answering when you ask an intimate question. And you probably also know those who anxiously ruminate about their lover's whereabouts but punish and resist them when they finally arrive home.

Sleep is separation from the other. We drift into our personal unconscious and are temporarily separated from those close to us, in a way, entering a "strange situation" in the unconscious world. Remember Mary Ainsworth's Strange Situation experiment that introduced a stranger to a room in which a toddler was playing with his/her mother and then the mother leaves the room? The toddler suddenly finds himself with a stranger and without his source of soothing (his mother), he becomes unsettled. Sleeping (as experienced through dreaming) can feel like we're in a strange situation without our bearings. I sometimes refer to sleep as a "mini death" based on the separation of self from other and the experience of losing consciousness. Indeed, the Greek god of sleep was Hypnos, twin brother of Thanatos, the god of death.

Research has shown that if a person has an insecure attachment style, he or she may struggle more with sleep issues than someone who has a secure attachment style.[76,77,78,79] In line with attachment theory is British psychoanalyst, D. W. Winnicott's, concept of the "holding environment." Ideally, parents create a holding environment for their babies when they are consistently caring and nurturing in response to their babies' needs. Winnicott made famous the concept that psychotherapy could heal a patient's psychological conditions, in part, by creating a holding environment in the therapy room. Regardless of a patient's upbringing, if the therapist was consistently attuned and caring to the patient, the patient would develop trust in the therapeutic relationship, thereby increasing the chances of a successful therapy experience and a secure attachment style.

While there are a host of variables possibly affecting a patient suffering from insomnia, it appears that those patients who didn't have a sufficient holding environment in their childhoods or even those patients who are temporarily suffering from an unstable relationship, which threatens their current holding environment, are more vulnerable to sleep disturbance. In addition, if patients with faulty or absent holding environments are also prone to hyperarousal (have a naturally more vigilant state of mind than others), they seem to be particularly plagued with occasional or chronic insomnia.

Let's look at Wendy Troxel and colleagues' work on relationship quality and sleep. Troxel's findings echo Winnicott's work on the importance of a holding environment. Troxel, Robles, Hall, and Buysse summarized the research on relationship quality and sleep, citing three studies that showed associations between attachment insecurity (particularly an anxious attachment style) and subjective sleep quality.[80,81] Their findings were echoed more recently by Laura Pagliani at the Sleep Meeting in June 2016. Her research showed that those with an insecure attachment style (those who are uncomfortable with relationships or overly dependent on them) had insomnia.

Troxel et al. also found that relationship *harmony* was an important predictor of sleep quality. In other words, regardless of one's attachment style, the more copacetic the relationship, the better one would sleep. People in healthy intimate relationships sleep better than those in conflictual relationships or in no relationship at all. Troxel explains: "Feelings of safety and security in the relationship may lead to decreased loneliness or negative emotions and increases in positive emotions, which may lead to better sleep quality." In addition, she muses that "in a high-functioning relationship, a partner is likely to be a powerful stress-buffer, down-regulating physiological and psychological stress responses, promoting salutary health behaviors, and deterring against health behaviors that could have a negative impact on sleep."

Consider the following two stories from my practice.

Kyle couldn't sleep *with* his partner, Angela. Every creak in the bed frame when Kyle's girlfriend shifted to every breath of air she breathed, the sensory stimuli was enough to drive Kyle crazy. He would just begin to drift when *jiggle jiggle*. Kyle's eyes would pop open and his heart rate would increase as he was yanked from a hypnogogic state of slumber into full-on wakefulness. Angela had readjusted her sleeping self and it was too much for Kyle to bear.

Two miles away, Sheri couldn't sleep *without* her partner. She'd have a couple of glasses of wine, pop an Ambien, take a bath, and listen to soothing music, but nothing! Without Ted, she felt uneasy and alone and, as a result, became extra vigilant of her surroundings. Is her boss going to reprimand her tomorrow for not having finished that document? Will Ted get bored with her? Is someone breaking in downstairs? But, when Ted was present, Sheri felt safe and secure. His presence cast a peaceful feeling over her life as if everything was going to be okay. She wrapped herself in his arms and slept like a baby.

How is it that Kyle and Sheri could have such polarized experiences when sleeping with their partners? It's not as if Kyle's partner snored like a freight train and kept him awake for obvious reasons. Angela was a quiet sleeper, really, and turned minimally in bed. Ted, on the other hand, was a big guy and took up quite a portion of the bed. But, instead of disrupting Sheri's sleep, he seemed to induce it. Why?

Kyle and Sheri were both hypervigilant (a state often associated with insomnia), but their respective attachment styles, in combination with their relationship situations, appeared to either activate or deactivate their hypervigilant state. Kyle's ambivalent (anxious-avoidant) attachment increased his hyperarousal with Angela in the bed. But, with Sheri, Ted's presence decreased her hyperarousal because of her anxious attachment. One could sleep with his/her partner, the other couldn't, depending on attachment style and holding environment.

To add fire to fire, Kyle and Angela weren't doing that well. They argued frequently, and lately there had been daily tension between them. To have an anxious-avoidant attachment style and to have relationship strife, puts one at risk for chronic insomnia because the *stress* of the strife is met with the *faulty resilience of an insecure attachment.*

Troxel et al.'s review of the literature found that relationship quality could impact a person's hypothalamic-pituitary-adrenal axis (remember this is the axis that regulates stress responses). And, when the HPA is dysregulated, it increases the risk for insomnia—a vicious cycle. Troxel also found that marital conflict can cause blood pressure and stress hormone levels to rise, thus potentially disrupting sleep. Last, a person's proinflammatory state seems to fluctuate according to relationship conflict. The more hostile the relationship, the more inflammatory markers were elevated. *Not only is this research testimony to the mind-body connection in relationship to sleep, but it illustrates how our attachment styles and relationship stress may have lasting, sleep-disrupting effects on our brains and bodies.*

I wonder about my infant memory of nighttime fear I described in Chapter Two. When my father soothed me, I felt safe. When he put me back into the crib, I became scared. When I had my own child, my hyper-arousal increased, pushing me into the world of chronic insomnia. My attachment to my nation was also suffering,

173

given the controversial 2000 election that resulted in having to recount votes, leaving many in an uproar, followed by the 9/11 terrorist attack in New York. Feelings of safety and security create calm, the feeling of being unsafe promotes vigilance. I believe my insomnia as an adult was influenced by my stressors at the time and by the hit my resilience took due to shaky attachment experiences.

So, here we are again, finding that stress, attachment, and now sleep are all interrelated. It behooves us to make psychological and emotional connections with one another a primary focus of our lives as it seems that when our relationships with one another are fragile or conflictual, we risk suffering from insomnia and bodily inflammation, which can promote disease. This is one of the reasons I often recommend couples therapy to patients that complain about stress and insomnia. The more honest, compassionate, and forgiving we are with each other, the better chance we have of both keeping stress low and creating secure attachments.

Work on Your Relationships with Others.

- Be compassionate. If there is conflict, look your partner in the eye and try to see her as someone who is struggling to find happiness, just like everyone else. See her for more than her behavior. Try to step into her shoes. I'm not advocating that you be complacent or not stand up for yourself. I'm talking about showing your partner you understand her.

- Forgiveness is also central to conflict resolution. Holding grudges produces tension and alienates you from others. Forgiving yourself or others for their mistakes is part of maintaining good relationships. It's the *repair* aspect of creating secure attachments. Forgiveness doesn't mean condoning what someone did to hurt you, it's lifting the burden of revenge. When you do so, you no longer ruminate about the harm done and how you're going to get back. With forgiveness, you create a more peaceful mind...one conducive to falling asleep.

Economics, Eating, and Endurance

"The bottom line: sleep is a promising target for obesity prevention."

—Harvard, School of Public Health

In addition to the pervasive problem of insomnia in the US, is the problem of sleep apnea. There are two main types of sleep apnea: Central Sleep Apnea and Obstructive Sleep Apnea. For the sake of this book, I'm going to talk for a minute about Obstructive Sleep Apnea (OSA), a condition in which one's air passages are obstructed at night, causing disrupted sleep. OSA affects twenty-two million Americans, the majority of which are caused by obesity. Why is this important?

I know from my work with thousands of people over the years that people often overeat in reaction to stress. In addition, stress itself can increase cortisol production. Cortisol binds to receptors on fat cells and activates an enzyme that turns triglycerides into free fatty acids! The result: stress can increase an individual's body mass index (BMI) even if he or she isn't overeating. Stress alone can make one fat, and being overweight is the most common risk factor for OSA.

Let's take a look at the obesity rates in the United States. In adults, obesity is defined as a body mass index of thirty or above. In children, it is defined as a BMI in the 95th percentile. Seventy-one percent of our country's adults are considered overweight, and 39.8 percent of that statistic (of the 71 percent) are obese.[82] In other words, nearly three-quarters of our adult population is overweight, and more than one-third is extremely overweight! Women are more likely to be obese than men, and black women are twice as likely to be extremely obese than white women. Money and work are the biggest causes of stress in American lives. And black women have lower income and poorer work opportunities than white women, which may explain why the obesity rate among black women is the highest in our nation.

In addition to these staggering statistics, the National Health and Nutrition Examination Survey stated that from 1980 to 2014 the childhood obesity rates increased with those in the six-to-eleven-year-old range tripling, and those in the twelve-to-nineteen-year-old range quadrupling. Excess weight in children comes with a price. In June of 2016, the *Monitor on Psychology* reported that children who are overweight seem to suffer from a host of executive functioning issues, anything from poor working memory to greater impulsivity.

What's more, children who were obese and suffered from metabolic syndrome (weight-related health issues), had less white matter in their brains and had thinner orbitofrontal and anterior cingulate cortices. What does this mean? White matter has been researched as important to learning and cognitive control.[83] Orbitofrontal and anterior cingulate cortices are associated with emotion processing. Less white matter and thinner orbitofrontal and cingulate cortices may make academic achievement more challenging, which can cycle back to increased stress, one of the main culprits when it comes to high BMI in the first place.

While the good news is that obesity rates among children have leveled off in the last few years (thanks to education in this area, including Michelle Obama's Let's Move program), 18.5 percent of American children are obese.[84] In addition, adult rates remain high.[85] It would appear that the responsibilities and worries that adults feel in our current culture, with our current circumstances, are not only forcing low-income folks to buy cheap, processed, fat-inducing foods, but that anxiety and depression lends itself to overeating, which puts a person at risk for OSA.

In a 2011 article in the *Journal of Obesity*, University of California, San Francisco researchers studied whether a mindfulness-based stress reduction treatment could actually decrease fat among obese people. They randomly assigned participants to either a treatment group (in which the subjects received nine classes on mindfulness and one seven-hour day of guided silent meditation) and a control group (who did not receive the course.) The results showed that the obese people who had the mindfulness course had a reduced cortisol awakening response (an indicator for cortisol levels in the body). And, reductions in the cortisol awakening response in the group that had the mindfulness course correlated with reductions in abdominal fat. What's even more fascinating is that the study showed the more people improved their mindfulness skills in general, the less abdominal fat they had, and the more people decreased their chronic stress, the less abdominal fat they had. This study makes us wonder how many obese people who suffer from sleep apnea are actually suffering from untreated stress.

If stress is related to weight gain and weight gain can cause sleep apnea, perhaps treating stress will not only help *insomniacs* sleep better, but it will help those with obstructive sleep apnea, as well. The relationship between the US economy, weight gain, and sleep apnea alert us to a cultural problem in the US worth paying attention to. In other words, the more people struggle economically, the more our country is burdened with health care costs to treat economically induced stress that induces costly conditions like sleep apnea. *Reducing economic and psychological stress may well reduce the occurrence of sleep apnea, which is a burden not only to our health care system, but to an individual's physical, relational, and emotional well-being.*

Is the Weight of the World Keeping People from Sleeping?

"We millennials are a lot like the Z Gens—we're born into this era of dread, in which we know everything is only going to get worse."

—Anonymous millennial speaking to his father in a Boston bar

Charlotte is a twenty-five-year-old woman struggling to make ends meet in a busy urban environment. She shares a house with two other women and works some sixty hours a week for an environmental organization. While she likes the cause she works for, the extensive hours and her boss stress her out. She doesn't have the option to quit or even take a day off, as she lives paycheck to paycheck, and she hasn't yet earned her vacation time.

Charlotte thinks about global warming and artificial intelligence and often lies awake at night worrying about the future of the planet. She also feels threatened by the vulnerability of being a single woman trying to make it in an expensive city without a car. The latter is important as sometimes, when Charlotte works late, she has to walk the four blocks from public transit to her house in the dark. This scares her. She stays vigilant as unprocessed memories of being sexually harassed while working as a waitress are almost nonstop since the media began covering the prevalent phenomenon of sexual exploitation of women. All of her repressed fear and anger about the harassment no longer hide out in the unconscious, but rather fester in this state of hyperawareness, which doesn't help her insomnia. Is Charlotte bearing the weight of the world on her shoulders?

Mason, a seventeen-year-old high school student, juggles the demands of school, football practices, drum lessons, and a part-time job. He is not unlike many teenagers these days whose schedules are overloaded. Most days, Mason doesn't get home until seven p.m., at which time he eats dinner and retreats to his room to start in on the two or more hours of homework his teachers have assigned. "Sometimes I just sit there, dreading what I have to do. I know it's gonna take forever and that I should probably start working, but I just can't," Mason says.

Mason's mother worries about him. "One time he fell asleep at his computer. I found him in the morning in the same clothes he wore the day before, head on his computer, sleeping. That's not right." She wrestled with pulling the drum lessons and football. "Why would I take away the two things my son is most passionate about? It's like punishing him for something that's not his fault."

The pressure on teens and millennials these days is enormous. They are growing up in a troubled and economically unstable world. They fear not having the resume that it now takes to get into the college and parents are right behind them, fueling their fears. I watched my own friends with teens become overly involved in their child's SAT and ACT scores, forcing them to get tutoring, take courses, study on vacation so as to earn the highest score possible. Parents often don't control their own angst and it bleeds onto their children, exacerbating the problem of teen stress in the US. The recent varsity college scandal in which parents paid off test administrators and college coaches to get their son or daughter into prominent universities indicates we have a problem!

Then there is the ubiquitous screen use. It's a fact: exposure to blue light before bed throws off your circadian rhythm, delaying the onset of melatonin, the hormone that helps us sleep. What teen do you know that isn't on his laptop or phone late at night? "I'm doing homework!" is the common response when parents yell at their teenager's closed door to get off the computer and get to bed. It's a painful vicious cycle and one that I, myself, have gotten caught in with my own teenagers. Worried parents often present as angry parents, which stresses and pressures the teen even more. The laid-back approach may not be much better. One of my friend's reports, "I just go to bed and say 'whatever,'" in reference to his son staying up until midnight studying. "What am I going to do about it?" Resignation is a common experience these days for parents with teenagers.

We create circumstances that allow little time for our teenagers to sleep and then scold them when they don't. Do we even know what success means when we urge our kids to achieve? In my book, success should be health and happiness. Is Mason healthy or happy? Not really. He falls asleep in class sometimes, often has a cold and experiences his social life mostly online. Maybe Mason feels the weight of the world on his shoulders.

Over the last two decades, I have noticed that my patients worry more about the stability of our world. Whether it be terrorism, global warming, mass shootings, or political divide, people feel unsure of what they can count on. I've illustrated how some of these worries have manifested with my patients: Jane and the yoga studio shooting, Peter and his fear of terrorism, my client who felt despair about global warming, and yet another client who is afraid to speak her native language in public since many Americans have recently and emphatically disapproved of immigrants. All of these people feel less than safe these days, and, like Charlotte and Mason, they all have trouble sleeping at night.

Americans also feel at the mercy of their smartphones. With pervasive media coverage on the ill effects of using your device before bedtime, many of us know we should put the smartphone down, that it isn't good for us. Overwhelmed as we are, though, we convince ourselves that checking email before bed will give us a head start on the next day. Tethered as we are, we tell ourselves that sleeping with our phones actually gives us peace of mind because what if we missed an important middle-of-the-night text or call from a family member, friend in need, or boss? How did we become such slaves? We want to feel less tired, sleep better, but can't seem to do what's needed for fear we'll fall behind. How do we break free from cultural norms that are killing us and from the weight of the world on our shoulders?

Define Your Values

In order to not be swept up by the pressures or perils of what may be happening in our culture, it is imperative that you know your priorities. One helpful exercise is to write a couple of paragraphs about how you would like your ideal life to look five years from now. Include desires about your physical health, relationships, job or career, living situation, activities, and so forth. Write what you truly desire. What is important to you? Now read what you wrote and ask yourself, "What can I do today to create that ideal life without overworking? In other words, if you want to hike Kilimanjaro, get sleep and exercise. If you want a good romantic relationship, work on being compassionate. Is how you spend your time in line with your values? Victor Frankl's book *Man's Search for Meaning* is one of the most profound books I have read. From the bars of his concentration camp prison, Frankl contemplates life and how to make meaning, despite horrific circumstances. While you may not be able to radically change your life on a dime, you can do something each day to bring more meaning and, therefore, feel less run by external circumstances or pressures. If Frankl could do this amidst torture and the threat of death, you can do it.

Grit and Mobilization

Insomnia is a circular phenomenon. Our minds circle without being able to achieve the calm we need to sleep. Anxiety, which is heavily associated with insomnia is, in part, a result of trapped energy. In other words, our mental energy gets trapped in our bodies as we tend to ruminate about things past and worry about things in the future without ever going anywhere. It's a merry-go-round that makes us believe we're moving in a direction when we're not.

Grit is about taking action. It's about deciding what you can do and doing it. It's about picking yourself up and saying (to yourself) with compassion, "I know your grades are falling, but tomorrow you'll get the help you need from your teacher to get back on track." Or, "It's brutal to work so many hours, so let's look at how to cut costs so you can decrease those work hours."

People often don't recognize how they abandon themselves, even when they would never abandon their child, their spouse, or their friend. They focus on the adverse circumstance and forget to attend to their own suffering. If you only focus on what you lost or the terrible mistake you made, and, in addition, you believe the outside world isn't a source of comfort, take yourself by the hand and decide to forge on.

I have one client who insists she needs a "plan" (of how to improve her life) each night so she can sleep. The plan fuels her grit. Grit is pulling yourself out of bed in the morning. It's apologizing when you've wronged someone. It's forgiving when someone has wronged you. It's being determined to make things go better. Make a pact with yourself to take action. If global warming, terrorism, or economics have you worried, do something. When we feel helpless, our sleep can suffer. I have one client who insists she needs a "plan" (of how to improve her life) so she can sleep. Decide what you can do to help your nation or world. Can you volunteer? Can you donate money to a worthy cause? Can you recycle more? When we take action, we ruminate less. And when we ruminate less, we sleep better.

Some people are kept awake by *others' emotions*. Like Velcro for the feelings of coworkers, family, or friends, you may wrestle with emotional discomfort at night, not realizing that your unsettledness is connected to *someone else's* sadness, anger, or shame. Perhaps you witnessed someone get ridiculed at work and you feel that person's embarrassment. Without realizing it, you cringe, remembering the incident, even though you weren't the one ridiculed.

Here are some mindful solutions to aid internal sleep hygiene:

- **Mindfulness-Based Treatment for Insomnia (MBTI)**

Psychologist and researcher, Jason Ong, PhD, created a mindfulness-based treatment specifically for insomnia. "People with chronic insomnia are so caught up in the problem. Many people have come to me saying, 'If only I could solve my insomnia, the rest of my life would go better.' And that's so much pressure," he told me. Jason knew that helping people detach from rumination, and their mental efforts to sleep, was key.

One MBTI exercise upon going to sleep is called trainspotting. With trainspotting, you imagine yourself on a train platform watching the trains go by as if they were your racing thoughts. When you inadvertently get hooked by a thought, such as, "I'm going to be so tired tomorrow if I don't sleep," take note that you mistakenly got on one of the trains, so to speak. Without judging yourself for this, simply step off the train and back onto the platform, where you can observe the trains (thoughts) without getting hooked by them. This is called metacognition, and it is incredibly useful for those struggling to sleep.

You can also use trainspotting in reference to alluring emotions, whether they be your own or the emotions of others you've absorbed. Let the emotions come through the station, observe them, but don't get on board. For example, if you feel afraid, observe

185

"there is fear" and watch it go by like a train passing through the station. Many people detach from emotions by denying them. They stuff what they are feeling and soothe themselves with food or alcohol. Trainspotting with emotions doesn't deny emotions, it changes your relationship to them.

- **Keep A Gratitude Journal**

Some of my clients wonder why they should feel grateful when life is so hard. I want to make one thing crystal clear here. Many people are suffering from profound losses that first need to be honored before they can get to gratitude. But, once your grief is expressed and soothed, mindfully focusing on gratitude can prevent you from a depressed or anxious state of mind. Gratitude reminds you of what exists after having grieved what you've lost. It helps you find silver linings and shows you that life is always renewing itself, even amidst death. Gratitude improves mood, which, in turn, improves sleep.

Keeping a gratitude journal entails writing down a few things per week that you are grateful for. Filling a journal with gratitude is like filling your heart with smiles. Try it. Think of one thing right now that you are grateful for and let it simmer there for a bit. Don't you feel calmer? Less stressed?

- **Look for the Good**

Because we so easily notice what is wrong in life, it helps to look for what's good. The fact that you are alive, that you have a roof over your head, maybe even a beautiful one, that the sun is out, that you have a friend are all good things to ponder. Tune into the warm cup of coffee in your hand, the trees outside your window that provide oxygen, the smile on a stranger's face. Noticing the good makes you happier, and when you are happier, you sleep better.

• Help Others

Helping other people makes us feel better and more connected. It also helps quiet internal chaos. Try to help someone each day. It may be as simple as holding someone's grocery bag so they can find their keys, picking up a dropped book, assisting your daughter with her homework, or cleaning the kitchen for a roommate who is overwhelmed. If you can do something for someone in your household before you go to bed at night, do it. Helping others increases positive social connection, which decreases cortisol and helps us sleep. It also helps develop secure attachments.

9

STRESS BEATS A BODY DOWN

"Stress can have wide ranging effects on emotions, mood and behavior. Equally important but often less appreciated are effects on various systems, organs and tissues all over the body."

—The American Institute of Stress

Marjorie sat on my couch, trying to hold back tears. Her voice cracked as she explained why she had come to see me. She worked in marketing at one of Seattle's high-powered companies where it was routine for most of their employees to work fifty to sixty hours a week. Her office environment was hostile, and she maintained she wasn't sleeping at night, perpetually worried about getting fired. She was also experiencing daily headaches, stomach upset, difficulty concentrating, and was battling bronchitis. To top it off, Marjorie's boyfriend had just left her, reportedly maintaining she was always down and he couldn't take it anymore. Marjorie told me she had gone to her medical doctor for help who had prescribed pain medication for the headaches and sleep medication for the insomnia. Marjorie was sick, worried, alone, and aging fast with nothing but temporary pill relief. When I looked at Marjorie's completed paperwork, I was stunned to learn her age. She was thirty-four years old, but she appeared a decade older. Marjorie was beyond stressed out. *She was burnt out and aging rapidly.*

While the majority of doctors' visits today (somewhere between 60 and 90 percent) are in response to patient complaints of stress, only 3 percent of those visits included stress management counseling. So, we're seemingly going to our primary care doctor because our stress levels are affecting our health, but we're not getting much help as to how to prevent stress from hurting our bodies. We're also not getting guidance on how to reverse the damage stress may have already caused our bodies. "Take two aspirin and call me in the morning" is not far afield from the advice many patients may get and what my client, Marjorie, got in the above story. Doctors often focus on how to treat symptoms more than they seek to ameliorate the causes. After all, medical doctors haven't been trained much on stress management and people still avoid psychotherapy because of the misconception that if you're in therapy you either can't handle life or you're mentally unstable. In addition, stress management training is undeveloped in most large companies, leaving many without the resources to cope with stress despite health insurance.

Clinical neuroscientist, Rogene Eichler West, PhD, uses a quantitative electroencephalography to identify functional brain dysregulations, including those caused by stress. One of the biomarkers of anxiety and oxidative stress is excess high frequency electrical activity above a region called the posterior cingulate (this region is the hub for almost all brain networks, including the default mode network I talked about in Chapter Three). She uses a technique called neurofeedback to heal and reverse the effects of stress on the brain, among other kinds of brain damage, such as problems caused by concussions or psychological trauma. Neurofeedback is a bit like going to the gym. Using principles of operant conditioning (a kind of learning like clicker training), neurofeedback trains your brain to rewire itself so that those whose brains are stressed can learn to calm down. Fascinating, isn't it? Eichler West illustrates that we are dynamic beings. "While we focus on neurofeedback to rewire a stressed brain, we also ask people to change the behaviors that got them there in the first place. Otherwise, we're just emptying water from a boat with a hole in it without patching the hole."

What's causing the hole in the boat for people today?

First, many Americans struggle to make ends meet in big cities like Seattle where the cost of living is high and barely affordable for middle-class Americans. As a result, large numbers of residents suffer from burn out as they try to make it by clinging to the jobs they have, regardless of personal satisfaction, or by working a second job. Marjorie was no exception. She was still paying down student loans and medical bills, and what she really needed was time off. Unfortunately, the two weeks of vacation time she was granted annually had already been used to take care of her ill mother and go on a not so satisfying trip with her boyfriend that ended in the break-up.

Second, people also don't eat healthily in the United States. We are a fast-food culture, which, as we'll find out, isn't good for us in more ways than one. As I discussed in Chapter Seven, unhealthy eating has to do with economics, but also to do with lack of education about the importance of healthy eating for our immune system and as a tool to prevent stress.

Third, while Missoula, Montana is apparently the most fitness-friendly city in the US, most Americans don't exercise much. The Center for Disease Control reported that in 2017, only 23.5 percent of Americans met the recommended guidelines for aerobic and strengthening exercise. When it comes to aerobic activity alone,

Americans do a little better—53 percent are meeting that guideline. If you have to choose between strength training or cardiovascular exercise, cardiovascular (or aerobic) activity will offset the effects of stress in a major way. It can increase serotonin (a sleep and mood-regulating hormone), for one, and protect telomeres (the caps on the end of your chromosomes that can determine longevity) for another.

Fourth, as I've illustrated throughout this book, our relationships with one another don't seem to be particularly strong these days. There is less eye contact, less physical contact, and less intimacy. Lack of strong relationship makes us more susceptible to stress and more susceptible to physical ailments which can only serve to increase our stress levels.

It took a good eight weeks of working with Marjorie before she decided to take the deep dive and quit her job. She'd saved enough money to live for two months. She had established trust in her therapeutic relationship with me and had secured her health insurance, so she could continue with sessions, despite leaving her job. Now, we could work on healing. But before I continue with Marjorie, I want to tell you a bit more about this chapter.

I described the biochemical effect of stress on the body's inflammatory markers in Chapter Eight. But there are other more visible effects that stress has on the brain. Both scientists who use functional MRIs to look at brains on stress and clinical neuroscientists, like Dr. Eichler West, who measure the brain's electrical activity, say they can tell the difference between a stressed vs. a non-stressed brain. Amygdales will either be larger or smaller. The posterior cingulate—which is part of the default mode network and the hub of all the networks in the brain—will be overactive. If the effects of psychological stress are this visible in the brain, how might those brain changes affect our mental and emotional health?

Not to mention our longevity? And what in the heck does all that have to do with our relationships with one another?

I discuss stress and the body by looking at three hot topics: the opioid crisis, our gut microbiomes, and our telomeres. If you've never used opioids or don't entirely understand what I'm talking about when I mention the gut microbiome or telomeres, don't worry, these subjects are still relevant to you. We cannot separate our minds from our bodies. They are inextricably connected, for the better good. If something goes haywire with the mind, it can affect the body and vice versa.

Pay attention, not because I'm going to bombard you with a host of burdensome and depressing statistics, but because I want to alert you to the effects stress can have on your brain and body, so you can prevent and possibly reverse them. I want to help you understand how stress may be affecting your gut microbiome and your telomeres, both of which can affect your mood, cognitive abilities, physical health, and your lifespan. I want to educate you about the invisible components of opioid use. I want to guide you on how to take of care of your body. I want to show you how taking care of your body can prevent stress. *That's the good news: there are solutions to the way stress can beat our bodies down.*

The Problem of Opioids
(Oxycontin or Oxytocin?)

"Because opioids were being given to me so easily and no one knew I was taking them (you can't smell them, you're not visibly altered), I became quickly addicted."

—Opioid Addict

Everyone wants to feel good. While some might find temporary comfort in an occasional melancholic state, there isn't anyone I've met who doesn't hope to attain happiness. But in a today's world, happiness can be overshadowed by the worry of global warming, terrorism and gun violence, by the stress of finding financial stability and by the difficulty navigating professional and personal relationships. In the United States, stress has gone up while connections with each other have seemingly gone down. This can make for an emotionally painful existence for many.

I've had many a client over the years ask, "Isn't there a pill to make the pain go away?" Well, yes, as a matter of fact, there are a few, and they reside in a family of drugs called opioids. Think hydrocodone, oxycodone, Oxycontin, Morphine, fentanyl, and the street drug, heroin. With the exception of heroin, these medications are used to treat pain in patients coming out of surgery or battling cancer but, because of their "feel-good" effect, they are well sought-after street drugs too. The magic of opioids is that they take away both physical pain and emotional pain.

When I think of emotional pain, I don't just think of patients who classify as depressed. I think of my anxious patients, my stressed patients, my lonely patients, and my patients who are grieving losses, hurting from break-ups. Emotional pain runs the gamut, and when we're in it, the same pain centers in our brains that activate when we're in physical pain also light up when we're in emotional pain. Both physical pain and emotional pain are processed in the anterior insula and the anterior cingulate cortex, interconnected brain regions that are also part of the "default mode network" I referenced in Chapters Two and Three. Returning to the cliché advice, "take two aspirin and call me in the morning," it appears that over-the-counter pain relievers, like acetaminophen, aren't just good for headaches— they take the edge off of emotional pain![87] *Do opioids have this same effect?* Andrea's story can help us understand.

Andrea was living what many viewed as a good life. She had close friends, a supportive family, and worked in a field that interested her, but she had trouble processing her emotions. So, she drank to suppress conflicted feelings, and as this habit intensified, so did Andrea's headaches. Sometimes mild headaches would worsen over the course of days, turning into stabbing migraine pain, rendering Andrea incapacitated. Other times they came on suddenly, causing Andrea to have to leave work early as she couldn't concentrate, let alone converse with anyone. One day, Andrea realized she couldn't manage the pain any longer and went to her doctor, who prescribed Vicodin. Vicodin contains acetaminophen and the opioid, hydrocodone. The acetaminophen is designed to increase the effect of the hydrocodone. Unbeknownst to her, Andrea began to use the Vicodin to treat both her physical *and* her emotional pain. She found the medication to be a wonder drug in that it made her feel happy and free like she'd never felt before. It had seemingly few side effects and virtually no hangover—as long as she kept taking it, which she did, and as long as her doctor kept prescribing it, which she did.

"I got it by the boatloads. Whenever I wanted more, my doctor would refill my prescription. The pills took away the migraine pain, for one, but they also made me feel euphoric, easy, more socially connected. Without them, I was stressed and tired and didn't want to socialize, but with them, I was relaxed, happy, and interested in being with people."

Being with others without conscious anxiety or fatigue is one of the benefits of opioids. They help people feel and be more socially connected. Sounds like heaven for those suffering from social anxiety and loneliness, doesn't it? In addition, opioids seem to help us hurt less when our social connections fall apart.[88] In other words, if a relationship fails and this causes heartache, opioids have been shown to decrease the severity of that heartache. Given the fact that our social connections seem to be suffering and that social anxiety and loneliness are on the rise (as illustrated in Chapters Five, Six, and Seven), the effect opioids have on loneliness and anxiety, puts Americans at heightened risk for opioid abuse. Andrea explains:

> *"It's easy to get addicted to opioids because they work like nothing else does. There is nothing that takes away pain like opioids and nothing, at the time, that made me feel so stress-free. If I was stressed, afraid, or worried about something, and even if I felt depressed, the Vicodin would take those feelings away. It helped me get through the day. It helped me connect with others more (or so I thought.)"*

The clincher is that no one knows you're doing it. There is no smell, no empty beer bottles lying around, no obvious signs of being "high" when you take moderate doses of opioid medications. It's an easy drug to disguise and, therefore, a common method to fool others and, even yourself, into thinking you're fine. Andrea was also still abusing alcohol, and one day her sister confronted her about it. Fortunately, Andrea fessed up to her alcohol abuse, took her sister's worry to heart and enrolled herself in an outpatient treatment program. She gave up the alcohol but kept using the opioids as no one knew about that addiction. And her doctor, *despite knowing Andrea was in drug and alcohol treatment,* kept prescribing them.

Outpatient rehab programs routinely drug test their patients. When they discovered the opioids in Andrea's system and heard the extent to which she had been abusing the drug (she had been taking 14 pills a day for months), they admitted her to an inpatient facility to detox. "The withdrawal from opioids is horrendous," Andrea stated. "You get really sick to your stomach. You get constipated. Your legs get restless. You have a lot of anxiety. You can't sleep. It's horrible."

It appears that in Andrea's case (and in the case of many people addicted to pain medication), opioid use begins by addressing physical pain, but it quickly becomes a vehicle for dulling emotional pain and increasing social connection. If a pill can ease the pain of loneliness and we know loneliness affects somewhere between 50 and 70 percent of American people, that pill will be a sought-after solution. If there is a pill that can instantly ease the pain of depression and depression affects one in every ten adults living in the United States, people will find it. If there is a drug that can reduce your suffering from anxiety and anxiety is the leading psychiatric diagnosis in the US, people will take a chance on it. We know we have a loneliness epidemic and that depression and anxiety are high these days. It's not surprising, then, that opioid addiction affects more than five million Americans today.

Andrea stayed clean for eighteen years after a successful detox, outpatient treatment, and weekly involvement in a twelve-step program. But around year twelve of her sobriety, believing she had a handle on her addiction, Andrea stopped going to AA. That turned out to be a mistake as, a few years after that, when she had shoulder surgery for a tendon injury, things changed. This time, Andrea was prescribed Oxycontin for post-surgery pain. She quickly relapsed into her opioid addiction, and by month four, she was still taking the prescribed meds around the clock because—you got it—her nurse practitioner kept prescribing them!

Despite heavy media coverage of America's opioid epidemic, lawsuits on the matter and increased education in the medical community, opioid medications are still easy to get. In fact, when Andrea would supplement her prescription by searching the medicine cabinets of friends, family, and acquaintances, she found that "a lot of people have those meds in their homes." The good news is that when Andrea's surgeon discovered she was still taking the Oxycontin regularly, many months after the surgery, he intervened and stopped her prescription. This prompted Andrea to get back into her twelve-step program. With the help of the program, she has stayed clean for over two years now.

How does she manage? "Now, as a yoga instructor, I've learned how to go into the discomfort I'm feeling, be it physical, mental, or emotional, be with it and breathe through it. I meditate. I make sure to get good sleep. I go to AA meetings regularly." In fact, Andrea teaches yoga in a nationwide program called The Yoga of Twelve Step Recovery (or Y12SR.) "When you're an addict, you escape from the moment and what you're really feeling, Y12SR helps you do the opposite. By practicing yoga and working the twelve steps simultaneously, Y12SR helps you become aware of physical and emotional sensations and be present with them, breathe through any discomfort, work through them instead of run from them. In Y12SR we take such tools practiced off the mat and out into the world where we most need them."

Programs like Y12SR are certainly helpful, but is there more we can do to address the stress of physical and emotional pain? Is there more we can do to prevent opioid abuse? I find it fascinating that opioids seem to produce similar feelings and relational states as the natural hormone, oxytocin. I talked about oxytocin in Chapter Five. It's the natural hormone that breeds positive social experience and makes us feel good. It helps us *build and maintain relationships*. Oxytocin is released when we offer one another physical affection and love. While it is sometimes prescribed to induce labor, we don't need a prescription to access it. In fact, just looking someone in the eyes can increase oxytocin. Doing something novel (and, yes, a bit stressful—remember some stress is good for us) can increase oxytocin. Practicing loving-kindness meditations can increase oxytocin. Helping others can increase oxytocin. Cuddling with your pet can increase oxytocin. And, what's more, oxytocin is a natural pain reliever.[89] When I think of building secure attachments, I think of oxytocin. Why? Because almost all of the aforementioned ways to increase oxytocin are also recommendations for increasing the health and security of relationships. The two, oxytocin and secure attachment, go together.

Think about this: if we focused more time and energy on fostering secure attachments, we would, by nature, increase oxytocin, which would keep us motivated to maintain those connections and possibly feel less anxious and alone. Remember the shoulder-to-shoulder concept of the Men's Shed? Or the South African value of "sawubona" that is inherent in Restorative Practices? If these places and practices were more readily available, perhaps we could more effectively address our emotional pain and loneliness. If meditation were taught in schools, like movie director David Lynch's *Quiet Time* program, we may learn (from a young age) how to manage discomforts, including physical pain. If prescribing doctors and nurses were better educated about stress and addiction, we may not have such an easy fix alternative. And if pharmaceutical companies were more regulated in their marketing of dangerous medications, we may have fewer opioid-related deaths. Consider the practices below to decrease your risk of opioid use and abuse or of any other substance that may not be doing your body any good. If you are already addicted or if Andrea's story sounds familiar to you, get help immediately.

Mindfulness-Based Stress Reduction. Molecular biologist Jon Kabat-Zinn, PhD, had meditated regularly during his adult life, including through his graduate education at MIT. As the story goes, during one of his meditations, Kabat-Zinn came up with the idea to develop a structured course that used mindfulness to reduce stress. Subsequently, in 1979, Kabat-Zinn founded Mindfulness-Based

Stress Reduction (MBSR), an eight-week program designed to reduce stress significantly and increase a sense of well-being. Research on the program began that same year and the results of that research, which continues to explore the effects of MBSR on a host of physical and psychological ailments to this day, have been nothing less than extraordinary. MBSR is a proven method of reducing stress and maintaining sobriety. Because relapse is a common problem among addicts who go through treatment (somewhere between 40 and 60 percent relapse within one year), MBSR, tailored for alcohol and drug addiction and, therefore called MBRP (mindfulness-based relapse prevention), has shown to significantly decrease relapse rates.[90] Many cities have MBSR and MBRP programs for addicts on an outpatient basis.

Meditation as a Part of Curriculum. In 2011, in an interview with Bob Roth, David Lynch said of meditation, "It's no longer a weird thing. It's getting to the point where it will be very weird not to meditate." Lynch has been a strong advocate of bringing meditation to schools and has had great success with his own Quiet Time program which teaches kids transcendental meditation.

As you've read, kids and teens have a lot on their shoulders today. They are our loneliest age group. If we teach kids, at a young age, how to meditate, we provide them with a free, accessible tool to instantly reduce their stress and increase their sense of connection to themselves and others. Meditation is possibly the most potent and cost-effective skill we can teach kids and teens. It can be a prophylactic against drug abuse and a possible lifesaver. Speak out and support programs like David's. He's right. Meditation is the wave of the future and needs to be a core part of a school's curriculum.

Sawubona. Seeing someone deeply takes time, patience, and intention. Many Americans don't feel they have time these days. We rush through life, dropping the kids at daycare last minute.

Sometimes, we begin the workday by dictating emails or checking our calendars while driving. Who has the time to stop, look another person in the eye, and listen to their story? Who has the time to truly, deeply see their neighbor, their son's teacher, or even the grocery store clerk? Doctors eyes are often locked to their computer screens as they type your symptoms into little black and silver boxes. This kind of disconnection from ourselves and each other can lead to profound loneliness, depression, and anxiety. For some, opioid use becomes the answer. But, what if like Zulu people in South Africa, we took the time to look the other in the eye and truly *see* them? What if we placed our children's faces in our hands every morning and, with smiling, compassionate eyes, sent them off to school with *sawubona,* instead of yelling down the hallway, "bye!" as they race out the door to catch the bus. Remember *sawubona* is the Zulu greeting that means "I see you and understand you" or what others translate as "we see each other."

Begin the practice of *sawubona*—of truly, deeply seeing the people you interact with each day. Look them in the eye and see them as valuable, fellow human beings. Making eye contact with this intention, can release the feel-good, social hormone oxytocin, which can make you feel happier and less alone. Opioids give us a false sense of connection with a high price. Looking each other in the eye with nonjudgmental compassion and the intention to understand has the potential to create secure attachments and to decrease the risk factors of opioid abuse: loneliness, anxiety, depression, and everyday stress. Start today. Look your son, daughter, mother, father, partner, sister, brother, coworker, neighbor, and strangers in the eye and honor their value. Fostering this simple yet powerful connection is a start to reclaiming the intimacy we all need to live healthy, drug-free lives.

Gut Feelings

"Follow reason, but don't ignore that gut feeling."

—Debasish Mridha, MD
Physician, philosopher, author

The gut microbiome is home to trillions of diverse bacteria. In fact, we have more bacterial cells in our bodies than we have human cells, most of which live in our guts. We each have an individual gut microbiome that is determined by how we were born (vaginally or via cesarean), whether we were breastfed or bottle fed, and to what subsequent environmental toxins (pollution, processed food, antibiotics) we've been exposed.

In addition, scientists are beginning to discover that psychological and emotional stress may also influence the makeup of our guts. Why is this important? Because the gut houses the majority of our bodies' immune cells and is often referred to as the hard drive of our immune system. That's right. Seventy percent of our immune system exists in the intestinal tracks of our bodies.[91] If our mental and emotional states are adversely affecting our gut microbiome, then our immune system will likely suffer, meaning not only are we more susceptible to getting colds and flus, but to developing allergies, chronic diseases and life-threatening illnesses. I know that's daunting, but, remember, I'm going to help you with this.

The gut also houses 90 percent of our serotonin (the neurotransmitter that contributes to feeling happy and that helps regulate our sleep-wake cycles, appetites, and emotions), which means these functions can be impacted if we are chronically stressed as stress reduces serotonin in the body. Additionally, the neurotransmitters Gaba and even dopamine, also responsible for mood, live in our guts.

Here is what is fascinating: *these neurotransmitters don't have to exist in the gut to get damaged by an unhealthy balance of gut bacteria!* The gut is directly connected to our brain via the *hypothalamic-pituitary-adrenal axis* (which regulates stress), the autonomic nervous system (which regulates our heart, digestion, and other unconscious bodily functions, as well as houses our fight, flight, freeze response to stress) and the *vagus nerve* (the longest running nerve in our bodies), connecting the gut to the brain and also regulating stress. These pathways between the gut and the brain are called the gut-brain axis or GBA, for short. So, the gut is the hub of our immune system, the center for our serotonin production (and other important neurotransmitters), and has the capacity to act as a "second brain," sending and receiving signals to and from the brain. The gut, and more specifically, the balance of bacteria that is in it, are pretty important to our brain health.

I spoke with Will DePaulo, PhD, who heads The Center for Microbiome Sciences and Therapeutics at the University of Washington. He explains that our gut microbiomes are unique to us individually. Like a fingerprint, each of us has a microbiome that is influenced by environmental factors, such as whether you eat McDonald's every day or whether you live in Los Angeles vs. Seattle, and, therefore, have different pollution exposure. (What you breathe in affects your gut, too.) He says that the balance of our individual baseline microbiome can get kicked out of whack—otherwise known as gut dysbiosis—if something internal or external causes certain bacteria to populate prolifically while causing others die. Take, for example, eating a diet high in saturated fat. The bugs that like to digest fat are going to grow, and those that don't will die creating dysbiosis from your original baseline. Another example is antibiotics, which, in their attempt to kill bacterial infections can wipe out whole groups of good bacteria, once again, creating an imbalance in our gut microbiome.

DePaulo says that our microbiomes are resilient. If we eat fast or processed food for a couple of days (such as, food with additives or sugary drinks), the microbiome will likely get imbalanced. And, we may not feel too well as a result. But, that temporarily imbalanced microbiome will bounce back when we start eating our fish and vegetables again. If we pound Big Macs every day, though, our microbiomes can permanently shift by turning bacterial genes on or off. While the type of bacteria may still exist in our guts, their genes may have changed, which can make the bacteria more virulent or inflammatory.

How does stress affect the gut microbiome? Do you remember from Chapter One, that when we feel threatened our hypothalamus (which exists at the base of the brain) is activated? It, in turn, activates the pituitary gland and the adrenal medulla to produce the stress hormones adrenaline and cortisol. This is the hypothalamic-pituitary-adrenal axis (HPA). From this chapter, you now know that the HPA is connected to the gut and when an abundance of the stress hormone cortisol is released via the HPA system, it can have an adverse effect on the gut microbiota. "Cortisol is a potent immune-suppressant," says DePaulo. "Because the gut protects you from pathogens, it needs to create inflammation against the bad guys while maintaining tolerance of the good guys, and if that gets out of whack [with chronic cortisol production] you start to have inflammation of the tissue which will impact the gut microbiota and lead to dysbiosis."

Hans Jangaard, ND, naturopathic doctor practicing on an idyllic island in Western Washington echoes this statement:

Stress taxes your sympathetic nervous system and when you're in a 'sympathetic' state it reduces stomach acid. If this becomes chronic, it can affect absorption and reduce digestive enzymes which then creates gut inflammation or an environment that is more likely to breed bacterial infections. If you wind up with chronic gut inflammation, that can then affect absorption of nutrients like B12, calcium or iron which further affects your body's ability to synthesize hormones or neurotransmitters like serotonin.

Dr. Jangaard states the most common complaint patients present with these days is fatigue and that fatigue is usually caused by stress. When I asked him how important a balanced gut was to improving energy and mood, he replied, "It's number one." Rogene Eichler West, PhD, expands on this theory. "A growing body of evidence suggest that if viruses or bacteria infect the vagus nerve [remember the vagus nerve has a bi-directional relationship with the gut and the brain] and this infected information travels up to the brain, it can cause inflammation as the brain's immune system tries to protect itself. This inflammation is then experienced as depression, anxiety, sleep issues and fatigue. Only recently, are we starting to recognize that many forms of brain dysregulation originate with chronic, low-level inflammatory disease."

Wow, inflammation in the gut can cause depression in the brain!

You know the phrase, "my stomach is in knots?" You may have said it yourself at some point. When our stomachs are in knots due to chronic stress, this can affect what is called gut motility. Gut motility is the movement of the digestive system necessary for grinding down food and passing it through our bodies. Particularly important here is that gut motility helps move waste from the small intestine to the large intestine. When the nerves or muscles in the digestive system aren't functioning properly, because they've been taxed by stress, a person can have motility problems which can affect an otherwise healthy balance of gut bacteria. In addition, opiate drugs are also known to slow gut motility, which can eventually create gut imbalance. Remember, gut imbalance can cause genetic mutations in the intestinal bacteria that lead to suppressed immune function or dysregulated neurotransmitter function.

What is most fascinating about the relationship between the gut microbiome and stress is that it appears to be bi-directional. In other words, just as psychological stress can disrupt a healthy balance of gut bacteria, an imbalance in gut bacteria (let's say, brought on by a poor diet) can reduce our resilience to stress and cause stress-related disorders such as depression and anxiety. One study tested this by studying the behavior of mice raised in a germ-free environment in which they didn't get the benefit of healthy gut bacteria. These mice had visibly more anxious and depressed behavior than their counterparts, who, through and after birth, were exposed to bacteria needed for gut health.

A particular condition called small intestinal bacterial overgrowth (SIBO) has gotten lots of visibility these days. SIBO is essentially gut dysbiosis in that it is an overgrowth of bad bacteria in the small intestine due to poor gut motility, diet, medications, and stress. SIBO is usually diagnosed by a naturopath via a breath test that determines your level of hydrogen and methane gases in the gut. These gases come off of bacteria and, if they are too high, they apparently indicate an overgrowth of bad bacteria. What naturopaths have determined is that if you have SIBO, it might be the cause of your illness—that is just about anything from irritable bowel syndrome to auto-immune disease to depression. Scientists find that altered gut microbiota correlates with IBS and seems to increase inflammation in the body, influencing psychiatric disorders.[92] Remember Dr. Eichler West said depression was an inflammatory disease?

Back in 2014, I injured my Achilles tendon from overuse, which resulted in a painful and very inflamed heel. At first it seemed like no big deal, but as various doctors tried to treat it, it got worse, requiring me to wear open-heel shoes in Seattle's winter. I became depressed and struggled to sleep well again. I began to wonder if something else was going on. But, between the orthopedic doc that put me on potent anti-inflammatories, the sports medicine doc that injected my heel with cortisone, and the rheumatologist that tried to treat it with oral steroids, my stomach began to feel pretty terrible and so did my mood. Ironically, the rheumatologist sent me to her nutritionist who, through testing, diagnosed me with SIBO, which she said was likely a result of the plethora of medications the rheumatologist and others had put me on to unsuccessfully treat the inflamed heel. In the meantime, that same rheumatologist wanted me to up the disease-modifying drug I'd been on for a dormant auto-immune disease as she was convinced my inflamed heel was indicative of a flair. Instinct told me not to increase the medication but follow the nutritionist's advice. It also told me to visit my naturopath, who, subsequently, treated the heel with a technique called prolotherapy.

Okay, things get a little technical here, so bear with me as I explain how the gut, the inflamed heel, and my mood were possibly connected. The nutritionist put me on a diet to starve bad bacteria and pumped me with probiotics that were supposed to repopulate the good bacteria. The naturopath used a combination of dextrose (sugar water) and lidocaine to inject my heel several times over the course of several weeks to draw healing properties to the site of injury. Jackpot! After a year and a half of hardly being able to walk and feeling pretty blue, I was cured. Not only that, but I had discontinued my auto-immune disease medications (as well as the anti-inflammatories), and I felt more clearheaded, slept better, and was happier.

Was it possible that the reported SIBO had been creating gut dysbiosis which, in turn, was dysregulating the HPA system, thus causing me insomnia, depressive symptoms, and stubborn inflammation in my heel? We'll never exactly know, but what I do know is that when I followed the diet/probiotic regimen and got off medications suspected of disturbing gut flora, I became healthier in ways I didn't anticipate. Dr. Jangaard states that "once you're *in* inflammation, it affects other parts of your body, making it hard to reset your system, but diet and reducing stress can help."

Dr. Depaulo would call the SIBO theory regarding my mood and insomnia inference in that there was no hard data determining what exactly was happening to my gut microbiome and whether or not it was connected to my physical and psychological symptoms, but some of the preliminary research is pointing in the direction of an interconnectedness between gut health and mood states. The fields of psychiatry and neuroscience are experiencing a paradigm shift as they increasingly look to the gut microbiome as a significant source of brain health. The concept that gut bacteria can have a positive effect on one's mental health is now called "psychobiotics" and has promise in the understanding and treatment of depression, anxiety, and even autism spectrum disorder.[93] Preliminary studies are looking at the use of probiotics, specifically lactobacillus, to treat depression and anxiety in lieu of psychotropic medication. Interesting stuff.

Don't get too get excited, though, as there is a lot of research still to conduct on the relationship between stress and gut health so the "don't try this at home" phrase applies. In other words, I don't recommend treating your depression or other ailment with probiotic therapy on your own, especially because probiotics can run the gamut and your gut microbiome may need a different probiotic than mine did. Depression is a complicated disorder with a big continuum and needs to be evaluated by a mental health professional. But, protecting yourself from some of the environmental factors that scientists *do* know play into gut health (stress, diet and chemical toxins, like pollution, pesticides, and pills—antibiotics, and steroids, in particular)[94] can only help, not hurt. Below are my guidelines on how to do that.

Eat Healthy Food to Prevent Stress

Research shows that food farmed using pesticides and foods with additives are potentially harmful to a healthy balance of bacteria in your gut and now we know gut dysbiosis can be a contributing factor to your ability to manage stress. It would behoove you to avoid foods grown with pesticides, additives, or meat farmed with antibiotics. In order to avoid pesticides, you have two options: buy organic or grow your own vegetables and fruit. It's unlikely that your average corporate employee like Marjorie has the time to grow her own food or that the apartment-living, single Mom trying to feed three kids has the time (or the place), but it is one sure-fire way to avoid pesticides. The other is to buy organic food as organic farmers do not typically use pesticides. It's not as expensive as you may think. Trader Joe's, Costco, and even Walmart all sell organic food at reasonable prices.

What about additives? In 2013, Britain's *The Daily Mail* reported that 80 percent of packaged food sold in the United States contain additives known to be hazardous to our health—*additives that aren't even legal to use in food sold in other countries around the world.* Foods with nitrates (think bacon, hot dogs, and other processed meats) can be replaced by foods that say, "no nitrates." Foods with Olestra (usually found in reduced fat potato chips) and food dyes (think gum, some sugary cereals, and sodas) can all be avoided for cheaper, healthier options. Drinking water and snacking on some carrots vs. fat-free chips can save your gut (and, therefore, your brain) from harm. Refrain from buying products that have the preservatives BHA,

BHT, and trans fat, as well as products that have additives like MSG, sodium bromate, high fructose corn syrup, and aspartame. Educate yourself and take the time to look at ingredients.

Gandhi said, "There is more to life than increasing its speed." Perhaps you can hold that sentence in mind the next time you find yourself flying through the grocery store and grabbing a jar of Pringles for your five-year-old. Because what eating healthily often comes down to is time. Isn't it better to take the time to shop and cook rather than running out of time early due to a faulty immune system? While it takes time to cook from scratch and while packaged foods are the go-to option for many parents who are trying to juggle kids and work, you can educate yourself on what is really necessary for you to buy and what you can do without.

If you decide to cook more from scratch, this may not only benefit your gut, but also the psychological environment in your household. Food is nurturance. Contemplate this for a minute. Cooking for ourselves and others can help create stronger, more meaningful connection because it is an intentional act of nurturance and promotes gathering and socializing, which are known stress-relievers.

Mindful Eating

Aside from being more conscious about what you buy and put in your mouth, you can also increase your awareness when eating. Like mindful meditation, mindful eating is a practice known to improve a person's physical and mental health. Here is the exercise: Take a small bite of food—anything that is healthy and sounds good to you—and slowly savor it in your mouth. Turn it around with your tongue, noticing the texture and the flavors of it. Chew it thoroughly. Now swallow it. Two things: 1) When you slow down and pay attention to the details of the bite of food, you enjoy it more and are likely to eat only what your body needs. 2) When you focus attention with keen awareness on the bite of food, you are practicing mindfulness which we know, from Chapter Three, is good for your body and mind.

Stress-Reducing Exercise for the Gut

Lie on your back or sit upright in a chair and place your hands gently on your abdomen, thinking of your hands as caring attention to this part of your body. Set in your mind the intention of releasing tension in your abdominal area. Now breath in deeply through the nose, feeling the rise of the abdomen and exhale through slowly through the mouth, imagining releasing tension and toxins from the body. As you breathe, see if you can imagine your digestive system, the twenty-five odd feet of intestine curling around inside your body, the enzymes that aid in breaking down food, the microbes that help maintain proper gut health. Visualize the intricate and mind-boggling workings of the stomach, small intestine, and large intestine and cultivate a thoughtful presence. Do this for five minutes. When you slow your breathing, you calm your nervous system and reduce the chances that cortisol will negatively impact your gut's immune cells. When you visualize the inner workings of your gut, you bring kind attention to an organ that may have been otherwise neglected, which can remind you to take better care of it. When you mindfully breathe, you also release tension, which can improve gut motility, and that, in turn, improves gut health.

Telomeres Tell a Story

"Our relationships and the neighborhoods we live in affect telomeres."

—Elissa Epel, *The Telomere Effect*

Remember Marjorie? She was stressed out, burnt out, anxious, and depressed. She looked ten years older than she was. What was happening to her body to make her age so fast? Elizabeth Blackburn, PhD, and Elissa Epel, PhD, would say her telomeres may have been shortening. What? Blackburn, a research scientist and professor of biochemistry and biophysics at UC San Francisco, discovered a biological enzyme called telomerase that dictates the length of our telomeres (little caps on the ends of our chromosomes). Together with health psychologist Elissa Epel, also at UC San Francisco, the two scientists wrote the book *The Telomere Effect*. It is a fascinating look into the inner workings of how our bodies age, by studying the relationship between our lifestyles, mindsets, and our cellular degeneration. Why is this relevant to stress? Because the authors purported that psychological stress shortens telomeres and shorter telomeres seem to predict earlier onset of disease, including mental illness, as well as shorter lives.

While some people may be genetically pre-disposed to shorter or longer telomeres, how you live can either lengthen or shorten the telomere length you were sort of assigned. In other words, if you deprive yourself of sleep, this causes stress on the body, which can shorten telomeres. If you worry incessantly, you can shorten your telomeres. If you feel chronically lonely, you can shorten your telomeres. If you are perpetually depressed, you are at an increased risk for shorter telomeres. If you're parenting chronically ill children, you may have shorter telomeres. If you feel unsafe in your neighborhood, you are likely to have shorter telomeres. If you eat poorly and never exercise, you won't benefit telomere length. Basically, anything that increases stress in the mind increases stress in the body and can shorten your telomeres.

Now a stressful day with your toddler or worrying about a presentation you have to give tomorrow isn't going to do major damage to your telomeres. In fact, it is likely not to have any effect on them at all. But if most days with your toddler feel stressful to you or you constantly worry about work performance, as examples, then your telomeres may shorten prematurely over time. Essentially, when we are chronically stressed, we age ourselves.

I saw it with my own eyes when I sat with Marjorie, knowing her biological age but witnessing her haggard appearance. I also witnessed what looked like age reversal as Marjorie began to take care of herself. Remember, that after Marjorie entered therapy, she made the decision to quit her taxing job. She allowed herself to rest but also began to exercise daily. The latter gave her the necessary downtime to let her nervous system calm and the serotonin boost to shift her depressive symptoms. I taught her how to meditate, and Marjorie began practicing regularly. This also had a likely hand in calming the nervous system and increasing hope. Meditation helps us connect with ourselves in a compassionate, nonjudgmental way. Under the gun of a critical boss and unrealistic work deadlines, Majorie had forgotten how to be self-compassionate and had never learned the freeing effects of suspending judgment.

While I'll never know what actually occurred inside Marjorie's body, what I can tell you is that after four months of the aforementioned practices, Marjorie looked vastly different than when she had come in. Her face was no longer strained and drawn. Her hair appeared healthier. She was more fit and carried herself with confidence. She was relaxed. She looked ten years younger than when she had first walked into my office. Blackburn and Epel state: "People who look older on average have shorter telomeres...looking older than your age—looking haggard—is a sign worth paying attention to." Marjorie had looked older, but now she looked radically younger.

While intuition may tell us that stress isn't good for us, Blackburn's discovery of why it isn't good for us and Epel's insight as to what we can do about it provide hope and motivation for many.

213

This is the good news: we have the means to change how we perceive and process stress, and there is some suggestion that this can protect our telomeres. You may not have control over all the stressful circumstances in your life, but you can control how you respond to them. And, with regard to telomeres, specifically, if you learn to take care of your physical, relational, mental, and emotional health, you can reverse whatever damage was done that a lack of self-care may have caused.

Exercise

It is a researched fact that exercise lengthens telomeres. In fact, if you have a lot of stress in your life and are worried about shorter telomeres, exercise may serve to offset the damage stress may otherwise do to these little "shoelace caps." I know, a number of you may just get tired thinking about exercise or convince yourself you don't have time. Let me give you some doable options here as exercise is not as unattainable or unsustainable as it may seem.

First, do something you like. If you like the water, choose swimming or rowing if possible. If you like the gym, get on the treadmill, elliptical, bike, or lift weights. If you like to stay home, download a yoga or Pilates video, get boxing gloves and a bag, jump rope. If you prefer to go places run, ride a bike, or skate, or find a recreational sport and sign up. Don't try to do something you hate. You likely won't sustain the habit. But, if you are getting some other joy from the activity, such as being outside or around people, you have a higher chance of engaging in the activity and sustaining the practice of it.

Second, start small. If riding a gym bike for thirty minutes seems time-consuming and exhausting, start with ten minutes. If taking time out of your day to go to the pool or lake feels impractical because of having to change, shower, and change routine, make it happen after or before work when you're already going to shower and change. And, if building in commute time at all for exercise is a deterrent, then put on an exercise video, run the neighborhood or even climb the stairs in your apartment building for twenty minutes.

Third, take it one day at a time. If you think: *I can't do this every day for the rest of my life,* you're likely not going to start at all. If you think: *Well, I already missed two days in a row, so I might as well give up,* you won't succeed. Think today and only today. *What will I do today for exercise?* And if you fall off the horse, don't judge yourself. Note what may have prompted the fall and get back on the trail.

Meditate on the Positive

If you're wondering why I have inserted mindfulness or meditation as a solution to just about every problem, it's because it is a healthy, free, do anywhere, anytime practice that can decrease stress immediately. In the case of telomeres, research shows that practicing meditation lengthens telomeres—and longer telomeres generally mean a longer, healthier life. Is that incentive to meditate? *You can conceivably reverse physiological damage that stress may have caused your body by sitting still and focusing your mind for a few minutes each day.*

There are many different kinds of meditation. There is bound to be a theme or practice that fits your needs. Peruse guided meditations online and get a taste of the variety. Here are some examples: You can do yogic breathing. You can do body scan meditations. You can chant mantras, silently or out loud. You can practice positive visualizations. You can do walking meditation. You can practice loving-kindness meditation. You can meditate to sound or music. Even prayer is a form of meditation. Those who say the rosary are meditating. The one stipulation here is to *learn how.* I give some references at the end of the book of places, both online and in person, to learn to meditate. And, remember, *it's a practice.* The aim here is not to achieve something, but to practice something, daily, to reduce your stress and lengthen your telomeres!

Additional Tips for Healthy Telomeres:

- Eat a high fiber, low-sugar diet, with plenty of vegetables, non-meat proteins, and omega-3s
- Don't smoke
- Limit alcohol intake
- Increase your relational support system (find someone to talk to about your stress)
- Know your values and let them guide your priorities
- See stressors as challenges to overcome instead of threats to fear

10

Twelve Tools to Tackle Stress and Strengthen Attachments

"If I could go back and do it again, I probably would've paid more attention to relationships."

—General Wesley Clark

Americans are swamped. We feel busy, short on time, and under pressure. Most of us believe we have more to do than time allows, and many say they feel *behind* on a regular basis. Stress is a common, everyday experience now with 60 percent of workers reporting they feel stressed more workdays than not. Approximately 57 percent of teens worry about being shot at school. Forty percent of eighteen- to nineteen-year-olds feel overwhelmed. In addition, according to the June 2019 issue of *The Wall Street Journal,* women worked longer hours, both inside and outside the home, and spent less time socializing and relaxing last year than ever before. And not without mention is the fact that many adults and teens bear the burden of having to save the world as they are bombarded with news stories about global warming, artificial intelligence, and nuclear war.

Relationships are the key to our well-being. They can provide us happiness, a sense of security, a supportive aid, a vehicle for laughter, a source of inspiration, and they make our lives meaningful. They increase our resilience to stress and motivate us to achieve our goals. They nourish us with love and create a net for us when we falter. Relationships help reduce the effects that stress can have on our bodies and minds. They are essential to longevity. They prevent us from being complacent.

I've explained attachment theory and illustrated how we can develop anxious, avoidant, ambivalent, or secure attachments to ourselves, each other, and our nation. Throughout each chapter of this book, I provide insights and guidance toward living a less harried, more fulfilling life. In this chapter, I summarize many of the concepts presented and give concrete strategies to develop securely attached relationships. Implementing these strategies will deepen and strengthen your connection to yourself, others, and the nation and create resilience in the face of life's stressors. Following these guidelines can help you feel less burdened, less anxious, less lonely, less apt to be overwhelmed by technology and information, and more likely to sleep better. If you implement these tools, you may even have fewer health issues.

I also provide you with an understanding of how certain exercises and lifestyle changes can reduce your experience of stress. While I've known many people who have quit careers, divorced their spouses, and moved out of the country in order to reduce their stress, you don't have to completely change your life to change your relationship to stress. It's true that making a 180-degree turn in life can sometimes be just what is needed to feel happier, but the smaller changes I discuss in this chapter can make a world of difference in how you perceive and process stress. They can also help mediate the effects of stress on your body and psyche so that you live a happier and healthier life.

The key is practice and discipline. Do what you can to establish a habit of implementing these tools. This will take patience, self-encouragement, and nonjudgment. You may get periodically discouraged. You will likely fall off the wagon. It's okay. Just get back on and keep at it. When you keep at something, you get better at it. The practices I outline below are based on research and my years of experience helping people who are stressed, anxious, lonely, tech-addicted, overwhelmed, sleep-deprived, and depressed. They are designed to help you navigate the current life stressors so you can live the life you want to live.

1.   Eye Contact

"I want to find one face that ain't looking through me."

—Bruce Springsteen

One of the simplest things you can begin to do today is to increase eye contact with others. Start with those closest to you. New parents: remember that the parent-infant gaze is what aids your baby's brain development. It also positively affects *your* brain's neurological process by releasing the feel-good, social hormone, oxytocin. Don't try to multitask while feeding, changing, or putting your baby in his crib. Increase the chances of a secure attachment by engaging with your baby, eye to eye. If he turns away, allow him to take this break as he is likely regulating his own tolerance of this intense stimuli. You don't want to *make* him look at you. Rather, you want to be there, ready to engage, face to face, eye to eye, when he's ready.

If you have or work with toddlers or older children, including teens, make sure to look them in the eye when you send them off to school in the morning, pick them up in the afternoon or when they ask you a question or tell you a story. Let them know you care. Close your laptop, turn off the stove, stop whatever you're doing, and take the time to have this personal, caring exchange each day with the children in your life. It's vital to their sense of security and will increase well-being in you too.

Accompany eye contact with empathic words. If I put my hands on my son's shoulders and look him in the eye without saying anything, he may benefit from the connection eye contact brings, but he'll understand more what I'm trying to communicate if I accompany it with, "I'll be sending you good vibes for your performance today." Think about it. If I was looking at my phone and said those same words to my son: "I'll be sending you good vibes for your performance today," he's not going to feel the full effect and intention of that sentence. To him, my phone is priority, as that's where I'm looking.

In addition, and for those who don't have children at home, take the time each day to *look at* your partner, mother, father, brother, sister, roommate, friend, boss, neighbor, or whomever you have contact with each day. Again, engage in some verbal exchange while looking them in the eye. This lets them know you're listening—that you care what they have to say or even that they exist. If your roommate laments that she failed her history exam, offer an empathic response, such as, "I'm sorry, is there anything I can do to help?" Some of you may be thinking, *I'm not a therapist, I can't talk that way.* Yes, you can. The powerful tool of eye contact with empathic statements promotes *seeing and communicating understanding* with people which reinforces your relationships with them.

Last but not least, take the time each day to look *yourself* in the mirror and send loving presence to yourself. Be kind to the eyes you see staring back at you. You might even say the words "I see you," or "how are you doing today?" Preoccupied with tasks or whether we're measuring up, we often forget to ask ourselves how we are really doing and give ourselves the chance to compassionately respond.

Eye contact entails:

- looking at screens less
- more in person contact
- intentionality

It is one small habit that, if you establish it, can help you feel more connected to yourself and others. Eye contact helps you:

- feel less alone
- feel more hopeful
- feel more motivated
- feel less anxious
- feel less depressed
- increases oxytocin in the brain which facilitates secure attachments

Laura Ling relayed a story of being held captive for months in a North Korean prison. Ling was transformed by moments of human kindness both from and to her enemy guards that left her with the profound experience of "what can happen when enemies get to relate as people." So, if serious enemies can find ways to connect and empathize with one another, you can, too. You'll be surprised how different it feels to look someone in the eye with presence and kindness instead of looking down at your phone or off to the distance. Getting used to facing instead of avoiding people is a step to building connections with each other and strengthening resilience to stress.

2. Release Judgment

"It wasn't until I accepted myself just as I was that I was free to change."

—Carl Rogers, psychologist

Now that you've learned to make more eye contact with people, increase your awareness of any judgments you have of them. Most judgments occur within the quiet of our minds. They aren't always spoken, but this doesn't make them less toxic. Maybe you're criticizing your coworker for being too chatty, or you're shouting expletives at the driver of the car that just cut you off, or you're passing judgment on your neighbor who never cuts his lawn. Take note and listen to the negative things you may be thinking or silently saying about others.

Also note what you say out loud to people. Are you telling your kid she is irresponsible because she didn't clean her room? Are you barking at your partner for forgetting to put gas in the car? Are you telling your father he's crazy for his opposing political thoughts? Become aware of the negative judgments you say to others and see if you can let them go. Consciously increase your awareness of them, note them as judgments, and release them. Then, open your mind to the person you were just judging. Think of him as more than his behavior. Think of him as a whole person, who, like you, may be trying to navigate the complexities of life.

Next, notice *self-judgments*. They will likely be more frequent and worse than you realized. Are you telling yourself you made a stupid mistake? Are you criticizing yourself for not exercising enough? Are you down on yourself about your work performance? Or worse, are you telling yourself you're a loser for being forty and not married? You'll notice judgments as they often come with the word "should" or "should've."

Whether real or perceived, judgment is responsible for a fair amount of anxiety. It is a threat. "If I'm not witty, people may think I'm not very smart." The idea that people would judge you as unintelligent is the threat that creates the anxiety. If you don't base your intelligence on whether someone thinks you're smart or not, you will not worry so much, or maybe not at all. Curiosity, not criticism, leads to illumination and growth.

It's simple, really. Negative thinking causes stress, and positive thinking releases it. And, remember, telomere length, gut health, anxiety, depression, overwhelm, insomnia, and your connections with others are all associated with stress. This makes releasing judgment one of the biggest stress-relievers I know.

3. Set Compassionate Boundaries

"Boundaries are a function of love and respect."

—Brené Brown, PhD, researcher and author

Tech boundaries:

We are at the mercy of myriad distractions these days. Technology is one of the most challenging distractions in our midst. Our phones are usually on our person if not nearby on a desk or in a purse. They ring, ding, and vibrate to alert us of a call, message, email, or notification. Our laptops and tablets are distracting culprits too. They are easily transportable and, for many, are often open and on. But you know now, from Chapters Six, Seven and Eight, that tech devices can both trigger our HPA system unnecessarily, as well as

223

keep us in an activated stress state because of our chronic exposure to them. They also don't do much for our sleep, *and* they can hinder relationships. (You know, the habit of half listening to someone as you fiddle with the phone.) If your devices are on and near you, you will get pulled in. If they are off or away from you, you are less likely to overuse them. Here are some ways to set boundaries around technology.

- Time boundaries: some people don't engage with their devices two hours before bed, others have them off while at work. You can make your own time boundary with tech in a way that makes sense for you. A person who works on an iPhone app may need his phone to do his work during the day, whereas a bank teller may not need it. Whatever you think the boundary should be, make it substantial. *Take several hours during your waking hours to remove yourself from your devices and try to stick to it as a daily habit.*

- Place boundaries: some people make a pact to not use their phones, even if handsfree, in the car. Others put them in another room at night. Others vow to not turn them on until they've had breakfast with the kids and sent them to school. Others don't allow their presence at any mealtime. Choose a place where you can separate yourself from your devices so as to relieve yourself of the stress information overload, blue light, and alert signals can cause. If you don't see or hear them, they won't cause you stress.

- Content boundaries: turn off notifications on your devices, sound signals, including the phone ring, and strip your devices of alluring apps such as games or news apps. Setting these boundaries makes it less likely that you will get derailed from the moment by content that isn't pertinent to the task at hand or to your well-being. People tend to wander when on their devices. The fewer apps or more restrictions you have on your phone, the less likely it is that you will overload yourself with unnecessary YouTube videos or news stories.

- Set boundaries *compassionately*. In other words, don't scold yourself into boundaries around tech. And, if you fall off the wagon, don't berate yourself for having done so. Setting boundaries around tech should be done without judgment and with compassion for how addictive, and therefore, enticing they can be. Devices have become like an appendage, and it's difficult to establish new rules for them. Be kind to yourself about it.

- Be particularly *compassionate with children or teenagers* about tech boundaries. Remember, we adults gave them the highly addictive devices and then expected them to regulate their use of them. Being kind doesn't mean being lenient. If you set and stick to a boundary, that is what matters. There is no need to speak harshly or critically to your child or teen about her tech use. Yelling at your child to put down the device isn't as effective as stopping what you're doing, looking her in the eye, and gently enforcing the boundary. After all, yelling raises the likelihood that you'll trigger a stress response in your child or teen. But, if you slip and approach your child harshly, repair the interaction. You can say, "I'm sorry, I shouldn't have spoken that way, let me start over." Repair is a powerful tool to securing attachments and reducing stress.

Work boundaries:

I discussed in Chapter Seven what may seduce people to work long hours or to ruminate about work when they're not working. But when work seeps into breakfast time, evening time and even sleeping time, you lose the ability to relax. Here are some ideas:

- Put a tagline on your email: You can actually set and state what hours you check your email, by adding that information to your signature line. For example, you can write, "I check email between 8:00 a.m. and 5:00 p.m.," or "I check email Monday–Friday."

- Set and stick to a work schedule: If you don't designate your working days or hours, you can end up working all the time. To counter this, make a point of not working on weekends or past 5:00 p.m. in the evening. Or, ensure that you take a lunch break every day without your device, so you can eat mindfully or visit with a friend.

- Take a vacation: Make sure to take vacation days every sixteen weeks or, if you can't do that, take "mini-vacations" as I discussed in Chapter Seven. If your work environment is so fragile that you think you'll lose your job if you don't work long hours, it's not a healthy work environment. Consider looking for a job that supports your well-being, one that doesn't work you to the bone or threaten to replace you for having a good work-life balance.

Relationship boundaries:
Sometimes we stress ourselves out because we do too much for other people or have a hard time saying "no" to others. We want to be liked, and so, we do favors, listen a little too much to a friend's woes and generally try to please. If this sounds like you, it is time to set some boundaries with the people in your life. Please remember that compassion is kind but not fickle. You can say to your friend, "I'm so sorry you're in a bind with work, but I cannot pick up your

kids today from school." Take care of yourself before extending yourself. This way, you won't burn out.

Intervene on worry:

Because anxiety is so prevalent these days and because worry is a huge part of anxiety, it's important to set boundaries around worry.

- Catch yourself in worry-mode. If you are practicing being present and having eye contact with others, you'll notice when you've gotten derailed and are lost in worried thoughts. If you're paying attention to your body, you may notice tension, an upset stomach or a pounding heart. You may have difficulty falling or staying asleep. Catch yourself in Worryland and then make a choice.

- Redirect attention. When you catch yourself in worry-mode, redirect attention to a task. When you move your mind off worry and onto a task, you disengage the default mode network, which is the part of the brain that likes to think negatively about your life. If you focus on a task or present phenomenon, like your breath, this kind of attention will reduce the tendency to worry.

- Direct your mind to something pleasant. Happiness research shows that if we intentionally direct our minds, like a flashlight, to something pleasant, be it the sensation of a warm breeze, the beauty of a vase of flowers, the smile on your child's face, we increase well-being. Why is this? Because with worry, our brains scan for danger, hoping that if we find the threat, fix it or eradicate it, we'll feel better. But because we can perpetually create dangers in our mind, we jump from one perceived threat to the next, keeping the HPA system activated. Worry is circular. So, focusing your mind on something pleasant releases your brain from its threat-focused state and creates a calmer mental state.

4. Be Honest

"Be yourself. Everyone else is already taken."

—Oscar Wilde

In a world driven by social media, it is easy to *hide* behind a persona, to *avoid conflict* with others, *have conflict* with others, and even to *lie* a little. Remember the concept of faces of the enemy from Chapter Two? If we don't really know each other, we can fool, disrespect, and project onto each other. We can also pretend to be someone we're not by embellishing. As a result, we damage trust and alienate ourselves from others. Without trust, there is no security, and without security, our resilience to stress gets compromised. Not only does dishonesty decrease resilience to stress, it causes stress itself to increase. Remember the section on robocalls, particularly the ones that try to scam you? Robocall scammers are an example of how dishonesty can set off alarm bells and raise stress levels.

Fears of being honest:

- Being honest can often feel vulnerable, especially if we self-judge
- We can't cover up flaws or mistakes if we are honest
- We risk angering or hurting others by being honest
- We risk criticism from others

Honesty can feel scary, frankly. But, that moment of fear is fleeting. If you are compassionate with yourself and don't judge yourself or the other person, even though the truth you speak may hurt or upset someone, being honest pays off.

Benefits of honesty:

- Being honest establishes trust in your relationships
- Being honest reduces anxiety, as you don't hold tension between your true and false selves
- When we're honest, we feel safer
- Honesty secures our attachments with each other

Think about the ways in which you've avoided someone because you didn't want to tell her the truth. Perhaps you stopped calling someone you were dating because the relationship didn't feel right, but you didn't want to tell her for fear you'd hurt her feelings. Or, perhaps you borrowed your sister's necklace without permission and lost it but didn't want to fess up for fear she'd freak out. Or, perhaps you tell the store clerk you're "fine" when she asks how you're doing today, even though your dog just died and you're heartbroken.

All of these avoidances and less-than-honest interactions increase stress. I often say to clients who suffer from anxiety that anxiety likes to fester in the gap between the true self and the false self. When you conceal what you're truly thinking or feeling to maintain a shinier persona, you can feel tense. You know there exists the possibility that someone will discover a hidden flaw or some falsehood about you—so you worry, scanning for cracks in the persona and putting more energy into its solidity. The energy it takes to maintain a false persona or hide what you believe are your flaws, creates stress in the body and taxes the mind. It leaves you more alone and less secure because you're not truly known.

On the flip side, telling the woman you're dating that she's lovely, but you don't feel the connection you're looking for, is hard but relieving. Telling your sister you borrowed and lost her necklace takes courage, but it will leave you less stressed than if you pretend you don't know what happened to it. Telling the store clerk you're not fine, but heartbroken about your dog, can release tension you may have felt from trying to conceal sadness. It also may give you the opportunity to have a moment of genuine connection with another human being.

Now, I'm not saying that you must tell *everyone everything.* Relationships need boundaries to feel safe. *Instead, the aim here is to face your fear of vulnerability without throwing yourself to the wolves. Speak from a genuine place. Be thoughtful about what you post or how you represent yourself on social media. Be sensitive and kind to others when they share their tender truths. The old adage that "the truth will set you free" may be a phrase to keep in mind the next time you ponder how to decrease stress and increase trust in a relationship.*

Most importantly, if you release judgment of yourself and others, being honest won't be so daunting. Employing the first three practices in this Chapter will make practicing honesty easier.

5. Widen the Lens

"Heaven is under our feet as well as over our heads."

—Henry David Thoreau

As you learned from Chapter One, stress causes our view to narrow. When there is danger, be it a car racing toward us, a bear rustling in the trees, the sound of a police siren, our brains tend to lose sight of our surroundings and hone in on the stressor. This can be helpful if we need to jump away from the car, avoid the bear in the tree and let the police car pass. But when our stressors are many and chronic, a narrow view is a liability.

Take, for example, a critical boss. If you interact with the boss on a regular basis and learn to fear his criticism as it feels dangerous to your self-esteem, a narrow focus will not serve you. It will cause you to think about the danger, in this case, your boss and his criticisms, constantly. You may end up replaying in your mind all the horrible things he's said to you. Or, you may go to great lengths to avoid him which entails being aware of where he is at all times. Thinking about your boss and his criticisms regularly will put you in a constant state of negativity and stress.

- Look around. Think about all that exists beyond the perceived danger. Doing so will cause the perceived danger to get smaller and your world to get bigger and happier. For example, there is an entire world beyond your boss's criticisms! There are coworkers that you enjoy. There is the work itself that interests you (when you're not criticizing yourself via your bosses echoed words). There is your husband waiting for you at home. There is your love of playing the piano. There is your favorite restaurant down the street. There is a toddler waving "hi" to you in the elevator.

- Look for silver linings. If your wife leaves you for another man after thirty years of marriage, you will feel devastated. You will need to grieve the betrayal and the loss. But, if you dwell on the loss and think that your life is ruined forever, you will be stressed and depressed. Dwelling is over focusing on the stressor, which, in this case, is the loss of your wife. Try to find a silver lining. Perhaps you had been trying for years to please your wife and gave up your own interests to do so. You can now rediscover your interests. Perhaps the tension between the two of you raised your blood pressure. Now separated, you no longer feel this strain, and your blood pressure has lowered. Perhaps there is another woman out there who will love and appreciate you more than your wife could—a woman you never would've met had your marriage kept going. Look for silver linings in even the most horrible of circumstances. There will be one.

- From a wound comes a spring. Some of our greatest traits and adventures come from the result of a wound. If you stay open, growth from hurt is not only probable, it's inevitable. Widen the lens to include how you can grow from hardship.

6. Practice Mindfulness and Meditation

"As we see the productions of our mind, we discover radical freedom."

—Jack Kornfield, psychologist and Buddhist teacher

If you are balking at these words, mindfulness and meditation, take heart, the points below can help.

- Mindfulness can be practiced anywhere, anytime. According to mindfulness guru, Jon Kabat-Zinn, mindfulness is "paying attention, in a particular way in the present moment, nonjudgmentally." You can be mindful while walking, eating, working, and even while having sex. Because presence, focus, and nonjudgment are the three most important components to mindfulness, it's no wonder your stress hormones chill out when practicing it.
- Mindfulness helps you to *be in time!* That's right, instead of feeling like you don't have time to be mindful, mindfulness puts you in sync with time. It brings you to the present moment so that you can engage in that eye contact, release those judgments, practice compassionate boundaries, choose to be honest and widen the lens. *When you are mindful, you slow*

down time because you are not thinking about the past or the future.

- Mindfulness gives you access to your "wise self." When we tune into ourselves mindfully, we are less emotionally reactive and tend to make better decisions.

Now that you've read the above, you may believe mindfulness is doable but still waver on whether meditation is a viable investment of your time, especially if it feels foreign. But meditation is scientific. It relies on a set of instructions that leads to verifiable results, some of which are:

- Meditation sharpens your cognitive skills
- Meditation improves your working memory
- Meditation decreases anxiety and depression
- Meditation decreases blood pressure
- Meditation increases telomerase
- Meditation makes us feel more connected to ourselves and others
- Meditation increases a sense of well-being and
- Meditation decreases stress.

Formally practicing meditation requires that you sit quietly and engage in a specific practice. Setting a timer is key as we can have a distorted sense of time or can quit early because we don't feel like meditating anymore. When you meditate, you sit or lie in a straight position and maintain wakefulness by focusing your attention. You are training your mind, so it takes effort. Meditation is not chilling out on the couch and daydreaming. Depending on the kind of meditation (and there are many), it focuses your attention on your breath, your body, mantras, or the world around you. It helps you note your mental, emotional, or physical distractions, and it brings your mind back to the intended focus each time without judgment. Meditation is a gentle, compassionate process. While it is a discipline, it is not meant to be harsh. Because there is no judgment, there is no pressure to succeed in meditation. It is a practice.

If you want to decrease stress and increase a secure attachment to yourself and others, I highly recommend you start a meditation practice. A daily thirty-minute practice is ideal, but if you can do ten minutes, do it. If you can do one minute, do it. While the more the merrier, even small amounts of meditation have produced verifiable, positive results.

7. Get Sleep

"The obsessive daily dose of self-doubt may be the single characteristic that separates natural born insomniacs from all others."

—Bill Hayes
Author of *Sleep Demons* and *Insomniac City*

The common cultural experience of having too much to do and not enough time causes many Americans to deprive themselves of a good night's rest. People are convinced that if they stay up late to get a few more things done, life will go better. But robbing yourself of sleep:

- Creates inflammation in the body
- Raises cortisol levels
- Damages the stress regulating systems that span from your brain to your gut, hindering your ability to manage stress
- Impairs your cognition
- Affects your mood
- Impacts your ability to regulate emotion

- Increases risk of contracting chronic psychological or physical illness
- Makes you more prone to accidents

In fact, sleep deprivation can cost you your life if you're not careful. But how much sleep is enough? The standard recommendation for adults is seven to nine hours of sleep a night. For teens, it is nine to ten hours per night. For younger children, it is nine to eleven hours a night. While most sleep studies indicate that cognitive, emotional, psychological and physical deficits occur with less than six hours of sleep, many studies make the case that damage begins to occur with less than seven hours of sleep. If you don't struggle with a sleep disorder, by all means give yourself the gift of sleep! Despite the cultural myth that work is more important than sleep because it demonstrates grit, there is nothing admirable, strong, or even smart about skipping sleep. In fact, doing so makes you less focused, more forgetful, moodier, clumsier, and it gives you the equivalent of a .05 alcohol content!

If you struggle with sleep apnea, get it treated. If you struggle with insomnia, consider the fact that the above six practices will help you sleep. That's right, *sawubona (eye contact), releasing judgment, setting compassionate boundaries, being honest, widening the lens and practicing mindfulness and meditation will all help calm your overactive mind.* In addition, here are other important sleep aids:

- Have good sleep hygiene (that is, make your sleeping space cool, dark, quiet, and comfortable).
- Try not to ingest caffeine after noon (that includes dark chocolate).

- Write down worries or to-do's on a pad of paper before going to sleep so you release them from your mind and have them logged for review at another time.
- Turn off and put away all electronics (ideally outside your bedroom).
- Get off devices two hours before bed.
- Don't drink alcohol late in the evening or too much alcohol (it disrupts sleep)
- Resolve arguments before bed—even if you can't agree, at least offer one another kindness and love so as to keep your attachments secure.

8. Eat Well

"Most people in our part of the world go through life in a pro-inflammatory state, and diet has a huge impact on inflammatory status."

—Andrew Weil, MD

Most of us know that if we eat well, we will be healthier. But do we really know what it means to "eat well" or "healthier"? In 2003, T. Colin Campbell and Thomas M. Cambell II published the book *The China Study: Startling Implications for Diet, Weight Loss and Long-Term Health*. It sold over a million copies. People clearly wanted the secret to a long, healthy life and must've been starved (no pun intended) for guidance! *The China Study* evaluated research done over a twenty-year span that looked at the relationship between diet and health. The general conclusion was that a plant-based diet produced the most optimal health while an animal-based diet (diets full of proteins, such as beef and chicken) was associated with chronic diseases.

Since then, research has continued to look at the relationship between diet and health. Medical and nutritional guru Andrew Weil,

MD, has always supported an anti-inflammatory diet. It is a diet heavy on fresh vegetables, healthy fats, such as olive oil, avocadoes, and nuts, rich in omega-3s, usually found in certain fish, and low in sugar. It is also a diet that many people living along the Mediterranean eat and, therefore, is also referred to as the Mediterranean diet. At the same time, Weil believes that food is more than sustenance; it is nurturance. In his book, *Eating Well for Optimum Health*, Weil says, *"Any recommendations for healthy eating that diminish or eliminate the pleasure of the experience of eating are certain to fail."*

Those studying the effect of diet on the gut microbiome propose a diet void of processed food, void of food with additives, low in sugar and low in saturated fats. They also support the foods that dominate the Mediterranean diet as these foods seem to maintain the balance of our gut microbiome, keeping a healthier immune system and bodily inflammation at bay. If a body has less inflammation, it's less likely to be in pain, less likely to be tired, more likely to be cognitively sharp and less likely to be diseased, anxious or depressed. It's going to have more energy. It's going to run more efficiently. The systems that regulate stress, such as the HPA or the GBA are going to function better, helping us handle the stressors we face on any given day.

And, like Weil indicated, it's not only about what you put in your mouth, but with whom and how you choose to dine. Here are some general guidelines for eating well:

• Reduce sugar intake, particularly processed sugar, but even sugary fruits, such as melon and apples. Fruits high in antioxidants and low in sugar are berries. • Reduce meat intake, especially red meat, cured meat, and processed meat, but you don't need to cut meat out of your diet entirely. • Reduce starchy foods, like potatoes, pasta, rice, and bread as they turn to sugar in the gut but continue to enjoy Mama's Sunday spaghetti and meatball dinner as the companionship of the gathering may be just as good for your health as eating a salad. • Eat whole grains. • Moderate your alcohol intake. Your wise self probably knows what drinking too much means for you, but the American Medical Association recommends no more than one to two drinks per day, depending on gender and body size. • Increase intake of vegetables…the more the merrier. • Increase intake of omega-3s (fish in particular). • Increase intake of non-meat proteins like nuts and legumes. • Eat dark chocolate, just not by the boatloads. • Eat healthy fats such as avocadoes, nuts, and olive oil. • Eat organic whenever possible…pesticides were not meant to be ingested.

*Consult a naturopath or nutritionist to find out if there are specific foods your body doesn't process well. Even if they are on the recommended food list, they may not be best for your personal body.

Gut health improves mood.

Anxious or depressed? Eat well to improve neurotransmitter and hormonal function. Remember how the majority of our serotonin, a mood-regulating neurotransmitter, lives in our guts? If our guts are imbalanced, so might this important neurotransmitter be. Remember that our brains are also connected to the gut via the vagus nerve? If our guts are healthy, they send healthier signals to our brains via this nerve. In addition, vagal tone improves when gut health is good. In addition, hormones like estrogen and testosterone regulate mood, and we know from my section on the gut microbiome that an imbalanced gut can throw these hormones off, wreaking havoc on our emotional states.

Mindful eating decreases stress and increases secure attachments.

What we eat is the first part of eating well. The second part is *how* we eat. We tend to fast in the US. I'm not just talking about

America's fast-food culture, I'm talking about our *pace* of eating. Many Americans don't take much of a lunch break. Others eat "on the go," shoving food in their mouths as they drive to work, eating dinner while watching TV, or eating while walking from one class to another. Our culture doesn't savor. We tend to devour.

This can be a problem for our bodies and for our minds. By multitasking during mealtime, we either ingest too much or too little, which can adversely affect our cognition and hormonal regulation. In addition, if we fail to truly enjoy what we're eating, we miss out on a possible pleasure each day, maintain an amped-up nervous system and deprive ourselves of possible connection with others. An Argentine cousin was in town recently. He watched in dismay as I wolfed down a piece of toast held in a paper towel while getting in the car. "Do you always eat on the go?" he inquired. I don't, but this was one of the rare days I was engaging in the typical American habit. I suddenly felt aware of its absurdity. What was the rush? Did I really have to wolf down the toast? Couldn't I have at least gotten a plate? And, why didn't I take the time to sit down and eat with him, a relative whom I may not see for many more years? This kind of behavior happens all too often in the US, but we can change that. Here's how:

1. Make time to prepare food, paying attention to how you're doing it, appreciating what you are making and thinking about the person you'll be feeding, even if it is yourself. We know from Harlow's experiments that the food itself wasn't enough to create a safe experience for the baby monkey. The act of nourishing yourself or another promotes good feeling.

2. Eat slowly and with awareness. Notice the food's flavors and the textures and savor them. When you eat mindfully, you will likely eat just what your body needs. You will enjoy the

eating experience more. You will make better food choices. Imagine slowly eating a handful of nuts vs. gobbling a fistful of French fries. If you can't imagine, try it.

3.   Dine with others when you can and create some ambiance. Perhaps set the table with flowers, light candles, and make the eating space clear of clutter. If eating with children, try not to discuss homework, job stress, chores, or any other topic that is business-related. Instead, talk about movies, goals, dreams, funny things that occurred, the world in general, or the meal itself. Keep mealtimes free from technology. That means don't eat with the TV on or even with the phone face down on the table. Studies have shown that just the presence of the phone is distracting. This kind of mindful eating helps build or improve your secure attachment to yourself and others. And secure attachments help build resilience to stress.

9. Exercise

"You don't have to be great to start, but you have to start to be great."

—Unknown

Okay, this can be a tough one for some people, especially those who have never formally exercised, for those who are convinced they have no time to exercise and for those who don't have the motivation to exercise. So, while I illustrate how to ideally build exercise into your life, I also help you with modified versions that aren't time-consuming or too daunting. The aim here is to help you desire exercise instead of dread it.

Research shows that if you get regular exercise (meaning thirty minutes or more a day of moderate physical activity, such as brisk walking, cycling, or playing soccer—essentially any activity during which you can talk but not sing), you live longer! In fact, one study showed that you could live 4.5 years longer if you engage in regular exercise. Another study demonstrated that if you combined regular exercise with healthy eating and no smoking, you could live ten years longer than those who don't adopt these lifestyle habits.

Elissa Epel and Elizabeth Blackburn reiterated this fact in their book, *The Telomere Effect,* when they found that "moderate aerobic endurance exercise, performed three times a week for forty-five minutes at a time, for six months, increased telomerase activity two-fold." Remember that telomerase seems to increase the health of telomeres, which predict longevity. If exercise can temper the effects that stress has on the mind and body, this is one of the best, free interventions on stress we have.

Did you know that if you exercise in response to feeling stressed, you will likely feel calmer for hours afterward? That is one immediate and remarkable stress-reducing intervention! We know that exercise increases certain neurotransmitters, like serotonin and dopamine, mood-regulating hormones that can help you feel happier and more motivated. It also increases oxytocin, which has both a natural pain-relieving effect and increases social bonding. In addition, exercise induces new neural pathways to form in the brain and increases growth in the hippocampus—the part of the brain responsible for memory, and that seems to be smaller in depressed patients.

When patients come to me suffering from depression, anxiety, or everyday stress, the first recommendation I often give is exercise. Not only has research shown that exercise improves mood just as well as, if not more than, many anti-depressants, my clients serve as testimony that it works. Some of the feedback patients have given in response to starting exercise routines are: "I feel *so* much better since I started running," "Since going to the gym, I have a lot more

241

energy," "Riding my bike helps me feel free and easy," "Weigh-lifting makes me feel strong and confident."

By exercising you are consciously doing something good for yourself, and the true self knows it. It's an act of self-care that sends a message to your mind that you are valuable. In addition, feeling physically stronger can promote psychological strength. Increasingly in touch with the power of your body when you exercise, you can begin to experience yourself as effective vs. helpless. In this way, exercise aids in a more secure attachment to the self which, as we know, creates more resilience to stress.

Furthermore, the mere presence of being among others while exercising seems to increase the benefit of exercise. In other words, if you exercise alone at home, you will likely feel calmer as the exercise itself has a calming effect on the nervous system. But, if you exercise among other exercisers, say in a gym, you will feel even more calm after your routine. Additionally, exercising outside, in nature, also enhances the benefit of exercise. Because nature reduces cortisol by itself, nature with exercise has a greater stress-reducing effect.

Here are some exercise options for all types:

- **The Lonely and Alone**

You don't have to have a community or a lot of friends in order to exercise with others. Join a gym, a running meet-up group, a yoga class, a cycling club, or simply walk a popular walking path are good ways to get among others while exercising. Research shows you don't have to have conversation with others to benefit from exercising among others.

But exercise does increase oxytocin, the social bonding hormone. So if you exercise, you may engage more with people as you naturally feel like doing it. Because engaging with others is something lonely people avoid, exercise can stop you from perpetuating aloneness.

And, when you connect with others, you are less likely to be negatively preoccupied with yourself.

- **The Busy and Overwhelmed**

You are the ones who insist you do not have time to exercise so you will need to get your exercise efficiently. Take the stairs instead of the elevator at your place of work or anywhere you go for that matter. Take a twenty-minute walk on your lunch break and then reserve ten to fifteen minutes to mindfully eat your lunch. Bike to work or school if possible. Dance to music as you cook dinner. Make a competition with your kids to see who can do the most jumping jacks and pushups. The idea here is to *combine and integrate* your exercise routine with other tasks or activities, instead of *adding* it to your to-do list.

- **The Tired and Unmotivated (aka Depressed)**

You have trouble getting off the couch to do much, let alone exercise. But, remember, exercise is the first line of defense against depression and fatigue. You'll need something accessible and easy in order to exercise, but your down mood could also profit from the added benefit of exercising in nature and among people. If you have to change clothes to go to the gym or the pool, this may be a deterrent. If you have to engage in an activity you're half-hearted about, you won't. So pick an activity that interests you, at least somewhat.

At the same time, depressed people are often tired of the same old, same old and could use some novelty in their lives. So, if you've always loved horses, but haven't learned to ride, now may be the perfect time. Because motivation is a problem, another option is to get out your front door, rain or shine, and walk to a reward (like a view, a cherry orchard, a friend's apartment, a favorite store.) If possible, walk for at least twenty minutes, but if that feels daunting, start with ten and work your way up.

Depression occurs when we repress aspects of our being, including emotions. Remember the origin of the word emotion is to move. If you want to break through your depression, moving the body is just as important as moving your perspective.

- **The Financially Strapped**

Not everyone has the means to afford a fancy gym membership, a swim club, or ski equipment. For those on a tight budget, you'll want to choose an activity that doesn't require a fee and doesn't necessitate a new wardrobe. Can you swim in a lake? Can you dance in your home? Can you play basketball at the local court? Can you save money on gas by walking to destinations instead of driving? Baseball players from the Dominican Republic are notorious for learning the sport using a broomstick and a bottle cap (a game called vitilla) as it is affordable and accessible for everyone. Get creative and have fun.

- **The Anxious and the Scattered**

Your mind races; it's hard for you to make decisions because you worry about which one is the right decision. Some of you are anxiously tethered to your devices, which can be a time suck. As a result, you have trouble making time for exercise. But, remember that anxiety is trapped energy, so expending some of that energy through exercise will help you feel calmer and clearer-headed.

In addition, directing your mind to an activity that requires focused attention means it *can't* ruminate. Take, for example, rock climbing. You have to be focused on each hand and foot placement, which engages the prefrontal cortex and disengages the default mode network (the part of the brain that tends to mind wander). Other

244

activities include yoga, weight-training, kayaking, jumping rope, and partner dancing, to name a few.

The main points here are: 1) focus the mind in a physical activity so it has less of a chance to ruminate and 2) remind yourself that expending energy through exercise will reduce anxiety.

• The Indoorsy Type

Even though nature is good for you, you don't have to go outdoors to get good exercise. Gyms, indoor pools, yoga studios, community centers with basketball or volleyball courts, Zumba classes, dance classes, and martial arts all offer the benefit of exercise with the added benefit of being among other exercisers. Feeling pressed for time? Exercise at home to a video of your choice before heading off to work or upon returning home. What a great stress-relieving way to start your day or evening!

• The Outdoorsy Type

The outdoorsy are the ones who often say when I suggest exercise for mental health, "I'm *not* joining a gym…they're sweaty and gross." The good news is you don't have to join a gym to exercise. In fact, you folks are going to automatically get that added benefit from exercising outside—where you prefer to be. While hiking, skiing, and swimming are great aerobic activities, so is walking through downtown, doing yoga at the park or feeling the wind in your hair as you cycle to work. Combine tasks. Shoveling snow or raking leaves, when done continuously, is exercise (and you're getting something done). The good news about liking the outdoors is that it is always just a few steps away.

10. Get in Nature

"All over the sky a scared voice is calling your name."
—Black Elk

The planet is suffering these days. Global warming statistics feel ominous. And, unfortunately, many people are too buried in the business of their lives and the pull of their electronic devices to notice or have the energy to do anything about it. The threat that planet earth, as we know it, may disappear is so unsettling to some that they consciously or unconsciously choose to ignore it. But, as you have learned from this book, an avoidant attachment is an insecure attachment and will not help you navigate the stressors of life, including the threat global warming poses.

Getting into nature has many benefits, but the one that stands out the most to me is that it has the potential to help you feel more compassionately connected to your world. And when we're more compassionately connected to someone or something, we want to take care of it. In Jungian psychology, Mother Nature can be interpreted as the archetypal "Great Mother," in that it represents fertility and fruitfulness—a place that provides new life and nourishment. This is particularly helpful if you are feeling stressed, depressed, anxious, or alone. Thinking of nature as a nourishing mother can help you use it to restore your tired, chronically stressed self. By feeling the sun on your face, the wind in your hair, or by listening to the rhythmic waves of the ocean, Mother Nature has the means to enliven and provide. Nature can be a place of grounding and connection.

We're living in a world of technological bombardment and information overload that causes us stress. Nature reduces stress. And, you don't need to spend days upon end or even hours upon end to get this stress-reducing benefit. Being exposed to nature, for as little as twenty minutes, can reduce your stress, worry, and sense of alienation. It can also improve your physical health. Let's look at how.

- Studies show that nature reduces the stress hormone cortisol.

It appears that if you spend just twenty minutes in some sort of natural setting, anything from the woods to an urban park, your cortisol levels and can significantly decrease. And, the more the better. In other words, while the decreases slow down after thirty minutes in nature, the more time spent in nature beyond the minimum of twenty minutes, the more cortisol levels continue to drop.[95] And, when cortisol levels drop, you feel calmer.

- Nature elicits a sense of "awe" which increases positive emotions.

You may have had experiences in nature that have made you think, "wow!" Looking up at a star-filled sky, viewing a butterfly being born from its cocoon, taking in a beautiful sunset. Research shows that when we experience this sense of wonder, otherwise known as "awe," we tend to feel connected to something greater than ourselves, we feel more grateful, we feel less anxious and we feel more generous toward others.[96] [97]

- Awe-inspiring experience of nature reduces inflammation in the body.

Not only does nature reduce stress hormones and enzymes in the body, it also seems to reduce inflammatory cytokines (proteins), which, when high, contribute to disease and aging.[98] Therefore, being in nature produces a biological pathway for increasing the chances of physical well-being. Because of the mind-body connection—what goes well in the body can positively affect the mind and vice versa.

Remember the gut-brain-axis is a bidirectional pathway through which bodily inflammation can affect stress-regulation and mood states.

- Being in nature helps us feel more connected.

Research indicates that when we experience the beauty and wonder of nature, we feel less alone. I often "prescribe" nature as a response to loneliness. If people get overly focused on the fact that they don't have a partner or are home alone on weekends, I encourage them to go out into nature where there is aliveness, motherly nurturance and sustenance. Some clients have reported feeling supported by leaning against a tree. Others report feeling held by sounds of the wind, the water, and the rustling trees. Others notice the aliveness of other fellow beings, such as birds, fish, and even caterpillars. Being in nature helps you recognize you are a part of a fabric, of something bigger that connects you to the world.

- Being in nature makes us want to help others more.

Helping others is a key ingredient in building and maintaining secure attachments. When we feel cared about and looked out for, we feel safe. In one experiment, conducted at UC Berkeley, researchers looked at helping behavior in students after the students spent some time looking up at a beautiful grove of trees vs. helping behavior in students that looked up at a building. What they found was that the students exposed to the trees were significantly more likely to help the experimenter who "accidentally" dropped a bunch of pens on the ground than the students who were exposed to the building. There are numerous other studies that echo the finding that when we are exposed to nature, even if is in the form of a few plants in a room, or a *video* of nature scenes, we are more helpful and more ethical in decision-making. Furthermore, being helpful, generous, and acting ethically lead to trust in any relationship, which helps facilitate secure attachment.

- Being in Nature Reduces Preoccupation with Everyday Concerns (Anxiety).

Because nature and, more specifically, the feeling of "awe," help us feel connected to something larger than ourselves, we tend to ruminate less about the little things. Less rumination means less worry and anxiety, which, in turn, decreases stress. When we're not preoccupied with the little things in life, such as whether a new coworker likes us or not, we feel calmer, more at peace. So, if nature can curb your preoccupation with daily troubles, why not use it as your anti-anxiety "medication"?

The key to using nature as a tool for reducing stress and increasing secure attachments is to be in nature without devices. If we sit on a park bench for thirty minutes but look at our email the whole time, we counteract the stress-reducing power of nature. If we allow ourselves to receive and send text messages while walking on the beach, we'll miss the prosocial benefits of nature. Being in nature means being present in a natural environment, physically and mentally aware. After all, part of the benefit of being in nature is getting away from the stress and constant stimulation of technology.

11. Employ Agency

"With agency you are active rather than passive, taking initiative and directing your life rather than being swept along."

—Rick Hanson, PhD
Psychologist and author of *Hardwiring Happiness* and *Resilient*

Agency is the willingness to pick yourself up when you've been knocked down. Maybe you've suffered an unexpected loss. Maybe you are exhausted by your unchanging circumstances, hurt by someone you love, afraid of being alone. When you're struggling, it is easy to get lost in a sea of depressed or anxious thinking. It can be hard to motivate. But, remember, we all have a wise self that knows what we need. If you pause and listen to the internal voice that is kind and supportive, it can help you take action to improve your life.

Here are the steps to employing agency:

- Identify trapped emotions. Remember that anxiety or depression can manifest because you are holding unexpressed emotion that rumbles around inside you like a caged animal. Try a mindfulness exercise that serves to identify emotion so that you can get clarity about what you're really feeling. Breathe into the emotion, release tension in the body where it might be held.
- Gather resources (both internal and external). Once you've identified your feelings, recruit an encouraging voice within that acknowledges them and responds to them with compassion. Let the wise voice from within help you decide what to do to benefit your well-being. Or, recruit the soothing company of a friend or help from a family member. Gather the resources you need to address the feelings you've identified.
- Be creative. Think about various ways to approach the problem you face. Think outside the box. Entertain all concepts, even if they seem impossible at first. For example, if you've lost your job, entertain the possibility of working for yourself, of moving to a less expensive city, of getting a headhunter, of going back to school. Thinking outside the box helps you see your setback as opportunity instead of seeing it as a limiting devastation in life.
- Make a choice. Some people fear decision-making because they're worried about making a mistake. But, when you're feeling helpless and at the mercy of circumstances, making a decision

helps you get off the floor and moving in a direction. I'm not suggesting that you decide your direction impulsively. If you've followed the steps above, you've given your situation thought, gathered resources, and have come up with a few options already. Now, you have to pick one. It's okay. Life's path is not a straight line, so choosing doesn't mean you're unable to change direction again in the future.

- Discipline yourself. Set a schedule or make a pact with yourself to follow through on the action you've decided. If, for example, you've been discouraged by your loneliness, and have decided to get out in the world more, hold yourself accountable to your plan. You may need to set reminders for yourself, such as post-it notes on mirrors or alerts in your phone that encourage you to get to that meet-up group, the gym, or an evening class. Try not to think about the action too much. That can cause rumination and further inaction. The Nike phrase, "just do it" comes to mind when engaging this step.

While you cannot control everything that happens to you in life, you can control what you do with it. Employing agency is critical. In other words, while it is important to acknowledge your feelings and to respond to them with compassion, it is vital that you move to get unstuck and renew your life.

12. Cultivate Hope

"I've failed over and over and over again in my life. And that is why I succeed."

—Michael Jordan

I'm sure that anyone reading this book has had at least one experience of feeling hopeless. Perhaps you've doubted you'd ever find love again after losing your soulmate. Perhaps you've lost hope about getting out of financial debt. Perhaps you've felt hopeless about a child who has fallen prey to drug abuse. It's a dark place to feel hopeless. It zaps motivation, makes you feel depressed, and it's stressful. When you are hopeless, you don't believe you can change your circumstance or perceptions, so you try less, which only serves to perpetuate hopelessness.

Hopelessness actually predicts lack of growth. People low on hope tend to choose an easier route in life, because, from the hopeless perspective, trying hard won't amount to anything anyway. When they do try, they also give up more easily than those with hope, which can result in a self-fulfilling prophecy. In other words, if you think you'll always be fat, but you try a diet and after a week you don't see results, you may get discouraged. You think, "why keep going?" So, instead of taking a different approach to weight loss, you give in and go back to eating burgers and fries, never losing the weight. Or, if you believe you'll always be single because you haven't met anyone yet to share your life with, your motivation level to get among others will be low. Because of this hopeless behavior, it will be harder to find a life partner.

How do you cultivate hope when you feel hopeless? Researcher and author Richard Snyder, PhD, believes there are three key components to cultivating hope:

- establishing goals
- recruiting agency (willpower)
- defining pathways to the goal

But, while these three tenets of hope have merit, subsequent research has found that people can have hope without engaging all three tools. In fact, many people have hope about a bright future without necessarily knowing how to make that future happen.[99] It does appear that having a vision is crucial to having hope. But what I've seen in my practice and what I've heard from people who have hope, despite dire circumstances, is that hope gets generated from connections with each other. Indeed, research shows that secure attachment predicts hopefulness.[100]

Hope is our ticket to keep going, to keep growing, and to finding meaning in life. Hope is so important to our well-being that, without it, living can be depressing and downright stressful. In a Greek myth, Sisyphus was condemned by Zeus to repeatedly push a boulder up a mountain only to see it roll back down again. This was his existence, for the rest of his life. Philosopher Albert Camus likened Sisyphus's predicament to what he considered the absurdity of our human condition—that we are really just repeatedly rolling boulders up mountains each day only to see them fall back down. Depressing. But, people like Victor Frankl, the Austrian psychiatrist who lived the horror of the concentration camp life in the 1940s, had a different view. He said, "When we are no longer able to change a situation, we are challenged to change ourselves." How we make meaning in life, how we strive, is deeply related to our connections with one another and ourselves.

At the beginning of my career, when I was working at an inpatient psychiatric hospital on the children's ward, I worked with a little girl who had been sexually abused by her father. I had asked her to draw the animal she liked the most and why. During this process, her emotions came to the surface. She told me that her father had hurt her. She began to cry. She pointed to her heart and said, "It hurts here, inside." I instinctively put my arm around her and said, "I know, it hurts your heart." That moment, although terribly sad, was also profound. It gave me immense hope. This five-year-old child, who had been so betrayed and violated, was not only able to identify

253

her feelings about the abuse but was able to trust another adult (me) enough to share those tender feelings. The connection we both experienced in that moment gave me hope for her future and for humanity in general. While neither I nor this little girl could change what happened to her, we could change how she moved forward in her life.

Hope can get us out of ruts and move us toward action. It takes vision. It takes imagining something desirable as possible. While it is debatable as to whether developing specific pathways toward your goal is necessary for hope, I've seen how having a plan, specifically that you can execute a piece of every day, is helpful. Here are some steps to cultivating hope in your life.

- Create a Vision: Think about and write down how you want your future to look, or draw images to create it. Envision the types of relationships you want and their quality. Think about romantic partners, children, parents, siblings, friends, coworkers, and so on. Envision how you will spend your time (what kind of job you'll be doing or where you'll be going to school or traveling). In other words, how do you want your days to go? Imagine your desired physical health, your mental well-being, your financial well-being, and your leisure activities.

Research shows that if you engage in this activity, it generates positive emotions. It also gives you a framework from which to contemplate what you can do each day to manifest your vision and reach your goals. If you picture yourself financially stable in three years, perhaps you can put $10 or $20 or more away each day into savings or retirement. If one of your goals is to have close relationships, perhaps you can make sure you practice honesty and vulnerability each day so as to build trust in new and existing friendships. Taking daily steps toward larger goals makes those goals more real and provides you with the feeling of effectiveness vs. helplessness.

- Generate Positive Emotions: Because positive emotions help cultivate hope, here are some ways to increase positive feelings.

1) Intentionally notice the good things throughout your day. People often get caught in negative narratives in which they perceive that nothing goes well, and that life is mostly disappointing. Intentionally noticing the good requires that you *pay attention* to the little things in life like the comfort of your soft T-shirt, the warmth of the sun on your face, a flock of birds flying in formation, and so on. When you have your head down, overly focused on how much you hate your job or how you wish you weren't single, you miss moments that can increase happiness and increase hope.

2) Think of a problem that nags at you. Now write a supportive letter to yourself, starting with: *Dear…*

Encourage and guide yourself to handle that problem. Imagine writing with commitment and loyalty to this person (you). Sign your name (yes, your name will be both in the salutation and the valediction as you are writing from you to you.) Now read it to yourself, preferably out loud. All of us have a nurturer in us, it's just a matter of pulling it out, and sometimes this exercise can do just that. To cultivate hope in life, we sometimes need distance from the devastation in order to see the life beyond. Writing an encouraging letter to yourself can assist you with just that.

3) Practice gratitude by keeping a gratitude journal in which you take fifteen minutes one to three times a week to write approximately five things you are grateful for. Gratitude can remind you that there are good things in your life. It can lift your mood and help you see the bigger picture.

Summary

Creating a secure relationship with yourself is the way to start reducing stress and increasing well-being in your life. When you learn not to judge yourself, when you practice self-compassion, when you take the time to look yourself in the eye, when you widen the lens and when you commit to living honestly, you are well on your way to increasing your resilience to stress. Eating thoughtfully and healthily, taking time to exercise, meditate, and maintain your personal environment all aid in developing a more cohesive and stronger *internal* relationship with yourself. And remember, exercise, diet, and sleep all have the power to reduce the stress hormone, cortisol, the power to maintain a healthy HPA system, and the power to keep our energy and mood states stable. These important bodily habits help us weather vs. absorb the storms of life. Most important, quality of relationship with yourself, through these healthy practices, creates an *internal holding environment* from which you can respond to stressors with sturdiness.

Developing a secure attachment to yourself will entail setting boundaries around technology, social media, work, and vices. Having boundaries will help you listen to your wise self and allow you time you didn't think you had. In turn, cultivating and tending to your relationships with others is equally important. The same practice of no-judgment, compassion, eye-to-eye contact, and honesty apply as you mindfully tend to all your relationships, regardless of intimacy level. This doesn't have to be time-consuming. It can be woven into your day in the *way* you talk to someone. Tending to relationships can be as easy as putting your smartphone down long enough to truly see and respond to someone. Cultivating external relationships does not mean being at the mercy of them. When you have compassionate boundaries, people are not a burden, they're stress-relievers.

Relationships are the key to our well-being. They create an *external holding environment* that allows us to take healthy risks, to grow, and to be more resilient to stress.

You can also create *a more secure attachment to your nation* and the planet through knowing that we are all in this together. Knowing that there are billions of people on earth, many of whom are outside your door, wanting connection just like you, is an inspiring truth. Being helpful to others can also secure your attachment to your nation. Donating money to, or volunteering for, desired causes increases happiness. But, even the simple act of helping an elderly person cross the street is empowering, both to you and to others who see you do it. Helping others increases well-being. And when we feel good, we are less susceptible to stress. Helping your planet by recycling, volunteering for your local park's organization, or by simply planting a garden, feels good and can draw you closer to it. In addition, living more closely aligned with the planet means being in nature more, which reduces the stress hormone, cortisol.

And when you're at a loss, when life beats you down, cultivate hope. Dream big, widen the lens to include possibility beyond what you typically see. Remember situations and even the grief of losses are temporary. Practice gratitude, look for the good, contemplate the positive so as to wire it into your everyday thinking. Awe inspires hope. Setting your eyes on a beautiful sunset, a baby bird learning to fly, or the complexity of a flower can help remind you not to sweat the small stuff so much. Being mindful of the sun on your face, the wind in your hair, the sound of a violin helps you ruminate less. Cultivating hope means remembering that tomorrow hasn't happened yet and, therefore, a world of possibility awaits.

ABOUT THE AUTHOR

Meg Van Deusen, PhD, is a licensed clinical psychologist and mindfulness practitioner in private practice since 1994. She has worked with children, adolescents, and adults both in inpatient and outpatient settings throughout the Los Angeles and Seattle areas. Her knowledge of and passion for attachment theory, mindfulness, interpersonal neurobiology, sleep and dreams informs her belief that meaningful connection with ourselves and others helps us handle stress. In her review of the literature and interviews with researchers, everyday Americans, and clients, she has cultivated a first-hand understanding of how our current American culture is creating barriers to human attachments and, therefore, weakening our ability to handle the stressors we face today. She believes that the ancient art of meditation, the recent research on happiness, and the simplicity of nature can, among other things, help us build resilience and calm during a time when disconnection has us lost in a worried world.

NOTES

[1] Tara C. Marshall and Nelli Ferenczi, "Exploring Attachment to the 'Homeland' and Its Association with Heritage Culture Identification," *PlosOne,* January 23, 2013, Vol. 8 (1). https://doi.org/10.1371/journal.pone.0053872.

[2] Al Gore, *An Inconvenient Truth: A Crisis of Global Warming,* (Pennsylvania, Rodale Press, 2006).

[3] Susan Clayton, Christie Manning, Kirra Krygsman and Meighen Speiser, "Mental Health and Our Changing Climate: Impacts, Implications and Guidance," *American Psychological Association, Climate for Health and ecoAmerica,* March 2017.

[4] "TED: The Economics Daily, Bureau of Labor and Statistics," *The U.S. Department of Labor,* 2009.

[5] American Psychological Association, "Stress in America: The Impact of Discrimination," *APA,* March 10, 2016.

[6] American Psychological Association, "Stress in America: The State of Our Nation," *APA,* November 1, 2017.

[7] James B. Stewart, "Facebook Has 50 Minutes of Your Time Each Day: It Wants More," *New York Times,* May 5, 2016.

[8] Sherry Turkle, *Alone Together: Why We Expect More from Technology and Less From Each Other,* New York, Basic Books, 2011.

[9] Allan N. Schore, *Affect Regulation and the Repair of the Self,* New York, W.W. Norton and Company, Inc., 2003.

[10] Barbara Streisand, Interview with Oprah Winfrey. *The Oprah Winfrey Show,* 2009.

[11] American Psychological Association, "Stress in America," 2016.

12   Stephen Porges. Interview with William Stranger, Dharma Cafe, "The Polyvagal Theory," May 15, 2013.

13 Marshall, *Exploring Attachment.*

14 Michelle Beauchesne, Barbara R. Kelley, Carol A. Patsdaughter, and Jennifer Pickard (2002). "Attack on America: Children's Reactions and Parents' Responses," Journal of Pediatric Health Care, Vol. 16 (5): 213–222, September 2002.

15 Michael Traugott, et al., "How Americans Responded: A Study of Public Reactions to 9/11/01," *Institute of Social Research, University of Michigan,* 2002.

16   American Psychological Association, "Stress in America: The State of Our Nation," *APA,* November 1, 2017.

17 American Psychological Association, "Stress in America: The State of Our Nation," *APA*, November 1, 2017.

18 American Psychological Association, "Stress in America: Uncertainty About Health Care," *APA,* January 24, 2018.

19 Jean M. Twenge, Thomas E. Joiner, Megan L. Rogers "Increases in Depressive Symptoms, Suicide Related Outcomes and Suicide Rates Among U.S. Adolescents After 2010 And Links to Increased New Media Screen Time," *Clinical Psychological Science*, November 2017, Vol. 6 (1).

20   Michael Otto et al., "Post-traumatic stress disorder symptoms following media exposure to traumatic events: Impact of 9/11 on children at risk for anxiety disorders," *Journal of Anxiety Disorders,"* 2007, Vol. 21 (7): pp. 888–902.

21 Sandee LaMotte, "Smartphone Addiction Could Be Changing Your Brain," *CNN*, December 1, 2017.

22 Harry F. Harlow, "The Nature of Love," American Psychologist, 1958, Vol. 13: pp. 673–685.

23 John Bowlby, *A Secure Base: Clinical Applications of Attachment Theory,* London, Routledge, 1988.

24   Schore, *Affect Regulation.*

[25] P. O. Svanberg, "Attachment, Resilience and Prevention," *Journal of Mental Health*, January 1988, Vol. 7 (7): pp. 543–578.

[26] Bowlby, *A Secure*.

[27] J. Abela, B. Hankin, E. Haigh, P. Adams, T. Vinokuroff, and L. Trayhern, "Interpersonal vulnerability to depression in high-risk children: The role of insecure attachment and reassurance seeking," *Journal of Clinical Child and Adolescent Psychology*, 2005, pp. 182–192.

[28] C. Colonessi, E.M. Draijer, G.J.J. Stams, C.O. Van der Bruggen, S.M. Bögels, and M.J. Noom, "The relation between insecure attachment and child anxiety: a meta-analytic review," *Journal of Clinical Child and Adolescent Psychology*, 2011, Vol. 40: pp. 630–645.

[29] G. Camelia Adams and Lachlan McWilliams, "Relationships Between Adult Attachment Style Ratings and Sleep Disturbances in a Nationally Representative Sample," *Journal of Psychosomatic Research,* January 2015, Vol. 79 (1).

[30] Cheryl L. Carmichael and Harry Reis, "Attachment, Sleep Quality and Depressed Affect," *Health Psychology*, October 2005, Vol. 24 (5): pp. 526–531.

[31] Laura Palagini, Giada Cipollone, Christopher Drake, Irene Mazzei, and Mauro Mauri, "The Role of Attachment Style in Stress Perception and Reactivity in Insomnia Disorder," *Conference Paper: Sleep*, 2016.

[32] E.P. Sloan, R.G. Maunder, J.J. Hunter, H. Moldofsky, "Insecure attachment is associated with the α-EEG anomaly during sleep," *BioPsychoSocial Medicine*. 2007; 1:20.

[33] W. Troxel and A. Germain, "Insecure attachment is an independent correlate of objective sleep disturbances in military veterans." *Sleep Medicine*, 2011, Vol. 12: pp. 860–865.

[34] Jeffry A. Simpson, "Influence of Attachment Styles on Romantic Relationships," *Journal of Personality and Social Psychology*, November 1990, Vol. 59 (5): pp. 971–980.

[35] Konstantinos Kafetsios and Georgios D. Sideridis "Attachment, Social Support and Well-Being in Young and Older Adults," *Journal of Health Psychology*, December 2006, Vol. 11 (6): pp. 863–875.

36 Sarah H. Konrath, William J. Chopik, Courtney K. Hsing, and Ed O'Brien, "Changes in Adult Attachment Styles in American College Students Over Time: A Meta-Analysis," *Personality and Social Psychology Review,* 2014, Vol. 18 (4): pp. 326–348.

37 Schore, *Affect Regulation.*

38 E.H. Hess, "The role of pupil size in communication," *Scientific American,* 1975, Vol. 233 (5): pp. 110–112, 116–119.

39 Mona Delahooke, Interview with Meg Van Deusen, March 10, 2018.

40 *Race to Nowhere,* directed by Vicki Abeles (2010, Reel Link Films).

41 *Screenagers: Growing up in the Digital Age*, directed by Delaney Ruston (2016, MyDoc Productions).

42 Victoria Dunckley, *Reset Your Child's Brain: A Four Week Plan to End Meltdowns, Raise Grades and Boost Social Skills by Reversing the Effects of Electronic Screen-Time.* (Novato, New World Library), 2015.

43 David Wallin, PhD., *Attachment in Psychotherapy.* (New York, The Guilford Press) 2007.

44 Tammi R.A. Kral et al., "Impact of short- and long-term mindfulness meditation training on amygdala reactivity to emotional stimuli," *NeuroImage,* November 1, 2018, Vol. 181: pp. 301–313.

45 Jean M. Twenge, W Keith Campbell and Elise C. Freeman, "Generational Differences in Young Adults' Life Goals, Concern for Other, And Civic Orientation, 1966–2009." https://www.apa.org/pubs/journals/releases/psp-102-5-1045.

46 Bianca DiJulio, Liz Hamel, Cailey Munana, and Mollyann Brodie, "Loneliness and Social Isolation in the United States, the United Kingdom, and Japan: An International Survey," *Kaiser Family Foundation,* August 2018.

47 i-Safe Foundation, *Cyberbullying: Statistics and Tips,* www.isafe.org/outreach/media/media_cyber_bullying.

48 Jean M. Twenge, Thomas E. Joiner, Mary E. Duffy, A. Bell Cooper, and Sarah G. Binau, "Age, Period and Cohort Trends in Mood Disorder Indicators

and Suicide-Related Outcomes In A Nationally Representative Dataset, 2005–2017", *Journal of Abnormal Psychology,* 2019, Vol. 128, (3): pp. 185–199.

[49] Yvonne Kelly, Afshin Zilanawala, Cara Booker and Amanda Sacker, "Social Media Use and Adolescent Mental Health: Findings From the UK Millennium Cohort Study," *EClinical Medicine,* January 4, 2019, Vol. 6: pp. 59–68. https://doi.org/10.1016/j.eclinm.2018.12.005.

[50] Melissa G. Hunt, Rachel Marx, Courtney Lipson and Jordyn Young, "No More FOMO: Limiting Social Media Decreases Loneliness and Depression," *Journal of Social and Clinical Psychology,* December 2018, Vol. 37 (10): pp. 751–768.

[51] Ethan Kross, Phillipe Verduyn, Emre Demiralp, Jiyoung Park, David Seungjae Lee, Natalie Lin, Holly Shablack, John Jonides and Oscar Ybarra, "Facebook Use Predicts Declines In Subjective Well-Being In Young Adults," *PlosOne,* 2013, Vol. 8 (8).

[52] Holly B. Shakya and Nicholas A. Christakis, "Association of Facebook Use With Compromised Well-Being: A Longitudinal Study," *American Journal of Epidemiology,* January 16, 2017, Vol. 185, (3): pp. 203–211.

[53] Michelle Colder Carras, Antonius J. Van Rooij, Dike Van de Mheen, Rashelle Jean Musci, Qian Li Xue, Tamar Mendelson, "Video Gaming in a Hyperconnected World: A Cross-Sectional Study of Heavy Gaming, Problematic Gaming Symptoms and Online Socializing in Adolescents," *Computers in Human Behavior,* March 1, 2017, Vol. 68: pp. 472–479.

[54] Stephanie Pappas, "The Psychology of Cyberthreats," *American Psychological Association,* February 2019, Vol. 50 (2): p. 44.

[55] Adam Gazzaley, "The Distracted Mind," *Lecture at UC Irvine,* January 22, 2013.

[56] Nisarg R. Desai, Kavindra K. Kesari, and Ashok Agarwal, "Pathophysiology of Cell Phone Radiation: Oxidative Stress and Carcinogenesis with Focus on Male Reproductive System," *Reprod Biol Endocrinol,* 2009, 7:114.

[57] Monica Anderson, "Six Facts About Americans and Their Smartphones," *Pew Research Center,* April 1, 2015.

[58] Connor M. Sheehan, Stephen E. Frochen, Katrina M. Walsemann, and Jennifer A. Ailshire, "Are U.S. Adults Reporting Less Sleep?: Findings from

Sleep Duration Trends in The National Health Interview Survey, 2004–2017," *Sleep,* February 2019, Vol. 42 (2).

[59] Shawn D. Youngstedt, Eric E. Goff, Alexandria M. Reynolds, Daniel F. Kripke, Michael R. Irwin, Richard R. Bootzin, Nidha Khan, and Girardin Jean-Louis, "Has Adult Sleep Duration Declined Over the Last 50+ Years?" *Sleep Medicine Reviews,* August 2016, Vol. 28: pp. 69–85.
doi: 10.1016/j.smrv.2015.08.004.

[60] Yu Sun Bin, Nathaniel S. Marshall, and Nick Glozier, "Secular Trends in Adult Sleep Duration: A Systematic Review," *Sleep Medicine Reviews,* June 2012, Vol. 16 (3): pp. 223–230.

[61] Carol A. Everson, Christopher J. Henchen, Aniko Szabo, and Neil Hogg, "Cell Injury and Repair Resulting from Sleep Loss and Sleep Recovery in Laboratory Rats," *Sleep,* December 2014, Vol. 37 (12).

[62] Michiaki Nagai, Satoshi Hoshide, and Kazuomi Kario, "Sleep Duration as a Risk Factor for Cardiovascular Disease: A Review of the Recent Literature," *Current Cardiology Reviews,* February 2010, Vol. 6 (1): pp. 54–61.

[63] Jerome M. Siegel, et al., "Natural Sleep and Its Seasonal Variations in Three Pre-Industrial Societies," *Current Biology,* November 2015, Vol. 25 (21): pp. 2862–2868.
doi: 10.1016/j.cub.2015.09.046.

[64] W. E. Copeland, L. Shanahan, C. Worthman, A. Angold, and E.J. Costello, "Generalized Anxiety and C-Reactive Protein Levels: A Prospective, Longitudinal Analysis," *Psychological Medicine,* December 2012, Vol. 42 (12): pp. 2641–2650.

[65] Ethan Kross, Jiyoung Park, Aleah Burson, Adrienne Dougherty, Holly Shablack, Ryan Bremmer, emma Bruehlman-Senecal, Jason Moser, and Ozlem Ayduk, "Self-Talk as a Regulatory Mechanism: How You Do It Matters," *Journal of Personality and Social Psychology,* 2014, Vol. 106 (2): pp. 304–324.

[66] Everson, "Cell Injury and Repair Resulting from Sleep Loss and Sleep Recovery."

[67] Carol A. Everson, Anne E. Folley, and Jeffrey M. Toth, "Chronically Inadequate Sleep Results in Abnormal Bone Formation and Abnormal Bone

Marrow in Rats," *Experimental Biology and Medicine,* September 2012, Vol. 237 (9): pp. 1101–1109.

68 C. Stamoulis, M. Haack, R. Surette, and J. M. Mullington, "Cortical Rhythm Modulations by Repeated Sleep Restriction and Recovery Sleep," *Sleep Meeting Presentation,* June 2015, Seattle, Washington.

69 Paula Alhola and Päivi Polo-Kantola, "Sleep Deprivation: Impact on Cognitive Performance," *Neuropsychiatric Disease and Treatment,* October 2007, Vol. 3 (5): pp. 553–557.

70 Paula Alhola and Päivi Polo-Kantola, "Sleep Deprivation: Impact on Cognitive Performance," *Neuropsychiatric Disease and Treatment,* October 2007, Vol. 3 (5): pp. 553–567.

71 A.M. Williamson and Anne-Marie Feyer, "Moderate Sleep Deprivation Induces Impairments in Cognitive and Motor Performance Equivalent to Legally Prescribed Levels of Alcohol Intoxication," *Occupational and Environmental Medicine,* October 2000, Vol. 57 (10): pp. 649–655.

72 W. D. Killgore, G. H. Kamimori, E. L. Lipizzi, and T. J. Balkin, "Caffeine Effects on Risky Decision-Making After 75 Hours of Sleep Deprivation," *Aviation Space And Environmental Medicine,* October 2007, Vol. 78 (10): pp. 957–962.

73 Yoo S.S., Gujar N., Hu P., Jolesz F.A., Walker M.P., "The human emotional brain without sleep—a prefrontal amygdala disconnect," *Current Biology,* 2007, Vol. 17: pp. 877–878.

74 Katherine T. Baum, Anjali Desai, Julie Field, Lauren E Miller, Joseph Rausch, Dean W. Beebe, "Sleep Restriction Worsens Mood and Emotion Regulation in Adolescents," *The Journal of Child Psychology and Psychiatry,* February 2014, Vol. 55 (2): pp. 180–190.

75 K. N. Kendrick, S. M. Gratzmiller, J. S. Silk, N. P. Jones, D. J. Buysse, and P. L. Franzen, "Altered Processing of Affective Stimuli Following Sleep Restriction in Adolescents: Pupillary Responses to Social Feedback and Sounds," *Presentation at SleepMeeting,* June 2015, Seattle, Washington.

76 G. Camelia Adams and Lachlan A. McWilliams, "Relationships Between Adult Attachment Style Ratings and Sleep Disturbances in a Nationally

Representative Sample," *Journal of Psychosomatic Research,* July 2015, Vol. 79 (1): pp. 37–42.

[77] Cheryl L. Carmichael and Harry T. Reis, "Attachment, Sleep Quality and Depressed Affect," *Health Psychology,* 2005, Vol. 24 (5): pp. 525–531.

[78] Wendy Troxel and Anne Germain, "Insecure Attachment Is An Independent Correlate of Objective Sleep Disturbances in Military Veterans," *Sleep Medicine,* October 2011, Vol. 12 (9): pp. 860–865.

[79] Laura Palagini, Eleonora Petri, Martina Novi, Danila Caruso, Umberto Moretto, and Dieter Rieman, "Adult Insecure Attachment Plays A Role in Hyperarousal And Emotion Dysregulation in Insomnia Disorder," *Psychiatric Research,* April 2018, Vol. 262: pp. 162–167.

[80] Wendy M. Troxel, Theodore F. Robles, Martica Hall and Daniel J. Buysse, "Marital Quality and The Marital Bed: Examining the Covariation Between Relationship Quality and Sleep," *Sleep Medicine Reviews,* 2007, Vol. 11: pp. 389–404.

[81] Carmichael, C. "Attachment Style…"

[82] "Obesity and Overweight," National Center for Health Statistics, *Center for Disease Control and Prevention,* www.cdc.gov/nchs/fastats/obesity-overweight.

[83] R Douglas Fields, "Change in The Brain's White Matter: The Role of The Brain's White Matter in Active Learning and Memory May Be Underestimated," *Science,* November 2010, Vol. 330 (6005): pp. 768–769.

[84] Craig M. Hales, Margaret D. Carroll, Cheryl D. Fryar, and Cynthia L. Ogden, "Prevalence of Obesity Among Adults and Youth: United States, 2015–2016, *NCHS Data Brief,* October 2017, No. 288.

[85] Cynthia L. Ogden, Margaret D. Carroll, Brian K. Kit, and Katherine M. Flegal, "Prevalence of Childhood and Adult Obesity in the United States, 2011–2012," *Journal of the American Medical Association,* February 26, 2014, Vol. 311 (8): pp. 806–814.

[86] Joshua J. Gooley, Kyle Chamberlain, Kurt A. Smith, Sat Bir S. Khalsa, Santha W. M. Rajaratnam, Eliza Van Reen, Jamie M. Zeitzer, Charles A. Czeisler, and Steven W. Lockley, "Exposure to Room Light Before Bedtime

Suppresses Melatonin Onset and Shortens Melatonin Duration in Humans," *Journal of Clinical Endocrinology and Metabolism,* March 2011, Vol. 96 (3).

[87] C.N. DeWall, G. MacDonald, G.D. Webster, C.L. Masten, R.F. Baumeister, C. Powell, D. Combs, D.R. Schurtz, T.F. Stillman, D.M. Tice, and N.I. Eisenberger, "Acetaminophen Reduces Social Pain: Behavioral and Neural Evidence," *Psychological Science,* July 2010, Vol. 21 (7): pp. 931–937.

[88] T.K Inagaki, L.A. Ray, M.R. Irwin, B.M. Way, N.I. Eisenberger, "Opioids and Social Bonding: Naltrexone Reduces Feelings of Social Connection," *Social Cognitive and Affective Neuroscience,* May 2016, Vol. 11 (5): pp. 728–735.

[89] Burel R. Goodin, Timothy J. Ness, and Meredith T. Robbins, "Oxytocin—A Multifunctional Analgesic for Chronic Deep Tissue Pain," *Current Pharmaceutical Design,* 2015, Vol. 21 (7): pp. 906–913.

[90] Sarah Bowen, Katie Witkiewitz, Seema L. Clifasefi, et al, "Relative Efficacy of Mindfulness-Based Relapse Prevention, Standard Relapse Prevention, And Treatment As Usual for Substance Use Disorders: A Randomized Clinical Trial," *JAMA Psychiatry,* 2014, Vol. 71 (5): pp. 547–546.

[91] G. Vighi, F. Marcucci, L. Sensi, G. D. Cara, and F. Frati, "Allergy and the Gastrointestinal System," *Clinical and Experimental Immunology,* 2008, Vol. 153 (1): pp. 3–6.

[92] Siobhain M. O'Mahony, Julian R. Marchesi, Paul Scully, Caroline Codling, Anne-Marie Ceolho, Eamonn M. Quigley, John F. Cryan, and Timothy G. Dinan, "Early Life Stress Alters Behavior, Immunity and Microbiota in Rats: Implications for Irritable Bowel Syndrome and Psychiatric Illnesses," *Biological Psychiatry,* February 2009, Vol. 65 (3): pp. 263–267.

[93] John F. Cryan, "Stress and the Microbiota-Gut-Brain Axis: An Evolving Concept in Psychiatry," *The Canadian Journal of Psychiatry,* 2016, Vol. 6 (4): pp. 201–203.

[94] Yuanxiang Jin, Sheng Wu, Zhaoyang Zhang, Zhengwei Fu, "Effects of Environmental Pollutants on Gut Microbiota," *Environmental Pollution,* March 2017, Vol. 222: pp. 1–9.

[95] Mary Carol Hunter, Brenda W. Gillespie, and Sophie Yu-Pu-Chen, "Urban Nature Experiences Reduce Stress in Context of Daily Life Based on Salivary Biomarkers," *Frontiers in Psychology,* April 4, 2019.

[96] Craig L. Anderson, Maria Monroy, and Dacher Keltner, "Awe in Nature Heals: Evidence from Military Veterans, At-Risk Youth and College Students," *Journal of Emotion,* 2018, Vol. 18 (8): pp. 1195–1202.

[97] Paul K. Piff, Matthew Feinberg, Pia Dietze, Daniel M. Stancato, and Dacher Keltner, "Awe, the Small Self, and Prosocial Behavior," *Journal of Personality and Social Psychology,* 2015, Vol. 108 (6): pp. 883–889.
https://www.apa.org/pubs/journals/releases/psp-pspi0000018.pdf.

[98] J.E. Stellar, N. John-Henderson, C.L. Anderson, A.M. Gordon, G.D. McNeil, and D. Keltner, "Positive Affect and Markers of Inflammation: Discrete Positive Emotions Predict Lower Levels of Inflammatory Cytokines," *Journal of Emotion,* 2015, Vol. 15 (2): pp. 129–33.

[99] Eddie M. W. Tong, Weining C. Chang, Barbara L. Fredrickson, and Zi Xing Lim, "Re-examining Hope: The Roles of Agency Thinking and Pathways Thinking", *Cognition and Emotion,* 2010, Vol. 24 (7): pp. 1207–1215.

[100] Bret L. Simmons, Janaki Gooty, Debra L. Nelson, and Laura M. Little, "Secure Attachment: Implications for Hope, Trust, Burnout, and Performance," *Journal of Organizational Behavior,* January 29, 2009, Vol. 30: pp. 233–247.
doi: https://doi.org/10.1002/job.585.

INDEX

STRESSED *in the* U.S.

Made in the USA
San Bernardino, CA
26 November 2019

60442107R00190